1969

This book may be kept

FOURTEEN DAYS

A fine will be charged for each day the book is kept overtime.

AP 8 '71			
MAY 5 '77			
GAYLORD 142			PRINTED IN U.S.A.

Electronic Circuit Action Series

TV VIDEO AND SOUND CIRCUITS

By Thomas M. Adams
Captain, U.S. Navy, Retired

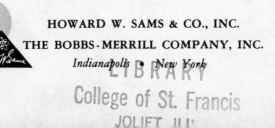

HOWARD W. SAMS & CO., INC.
THE BOBBS-MERRILL COMPANY, INC.
Indianapolis • New York

SECOND EDITION

FIRST PRINTING — JULY, 1966
SECOND PRINTING — JANUARY, 1967

Library of Congress Catalog Card Number: 66-25342

PREFACE

This book, along with the companion text, *TV Sync and Deflection Circuit Actions*, provides a complete coverage of the fundamental circuits used in VHF television receivers. No attempt has been made to include the many variations in specific circuits used by the numerous receiver manufacturers. However, those circuits which are most widely used have been chosen for detailed discussion and qualitative analysis. The analytical method used follows the same format as all prior volumes in this Series. This method clearly identifies each and every electron current flowing in the circuit under discussion, and shows what happens to these currents during each moment of circuit operation.

No electron current is completely independent and divorced from all other electron currents in a circuit. Thus, when the complete path of any current is analyzed, along with the reasons why that current is flowing, you will inevitably discover the function or purpose of that current. When you can visualize the actions of all of the electron currents in any circuit, you can fully understand that circuit. This understanding can be achieved without prior background in mathematical terminology and without prior technical experience in working with electronic equipment. Such an understanding is, and should be, an invaluable prelude to further studies in the field of electronics. The author holds the firm conviction that this type of understanding should come *before* any further studies are undertaken.

The first chapter of this book is devoted to a discussion of the video signal and how images are reproduced on the picture-tube screen. The next two chapters cover the different types of circuitry employed in the tuner section of typical TV receivers. Chapters 4 and 5 discuss the processing of the signal from the tuner to the picture tube, including the video-IF amplifiers, video detector, video amplifier, and picture-tube signal circuitry. Chapters 6 and 7 are devoted to the various types of sound circuitry employed in TV receivers. The more common power-supply circuits are discussed in the final chapter.

The diagrams in this text, and in all prior texts of this series, should not be considered as merely diagrams of circuit connections; they are diagrams of circuit *actions*. The movements of the parts in a piece of machinery cannot be visualized by looking at the external housing. Likewise, the actions occurring within circuit components cannot be visualized by looking at those components or at the accepted symbols for them. (The symbols intrinsically convey the same amount of information as, but no more than, a picture of the actual component would.) When all electron currents are portrayed, the reader has the best possible chance of understanding the complete operation of that circuit. From this point he can go on to master the more complex terminology frequently used in textbooks.

In other words, the terminology of electronics can be learned with relative ease from an understanding of the operational details involved; whereas, the operational details of circuit actions cannot be learned, except with the greatest of difficulty, from the abstract terminology alone. Because of the enormous simplification in the teaching-learning process used in this series, these books are considered to be neither too advanced for high school or technical institute studies, nor too elementary for college engineering instruction.

THOMAS M. ADAMS

TABLE OF CONTENTS

CHAPTER 1

CHAPTER 2

CHAPTER 3

CHAPTER 4

CHAPTER 5

CHAPTER 6

CHAPTER 7

CHAPTER 8

Chapter 1

THE COMPOSITE
TELEVISION SIGNAL

In the United States a frequency band 6 megacycles (mc) wide
is allocated for the standard television signal. This 6 megacycles
must include the guard or isolation space. There are twelve channels allocated in the very high frequency (VHF) band and 70
additional channels in the ultrahigh frequency (UHF) band. The
great bulk of present-day commercial television is handled by
the 12 VHF channels (Table 1-1). The seventy UHF channels,
which cover the frequency band from 470 to 890 mc, represent a
great potential for ultimate expansion of the television industry.

Table 1-1. Frequency Limits of VHF TV Channels

Channel No.	Frequency Limits (mc)	Channel No.	Frequency Limits (mc)
2	54-60	8	180-186
3	60-66	9	186-192
4	66-72	10	192-198
5	76-82	11	198-204
6	82-88	12	204-210
7	174-180	13	210-216

There are three essential types of intelligence, or information,
which are transmitted by the television transmitter and which
must be received at the receiver. All of this information must be
confined within the 6-mc channel bandwidth. The three types of
information in the carrier signal are the picture information,
picture synchronizing information, and the audio (sound) information.

TV RECEIVER

A block diagram of the portion of the receiver to be covered in this book is given in Fig. 1-1. (The remainder of the TV receiver is discussed in the companion volume, *TV Sync and Deflection Circuit Actions.*) Only the tuner is concerned with the channel frequencies given previously. In this section the incoming signal is amplified and heterodyned, or mixed, with a local oscillator to produce a lower video intermediate-frequency (IF) signal.

All three types of intelligence—picture, synchronization, and sound—are converted to the lower frequency. The video IF bandwidth is the same as the channel frequency, or 6 mc. However, the IF is the same for all channels. In most modern TV receivers the video IF band extends from 41 to 47 mc. The advantages of using a single video IF band will be discussed in the chapter on video IF amplifiers.

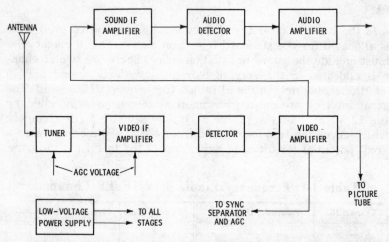

Fig. 1-1. Block diagram of the portion of the TV receiver which will be covered in this book.

In a typical intercarrier receiver the three types of information are carried together through the video IF amplifier stages and "separated" from each other in the vicinity of the video detector. After the separation process, the three types of signals go to three different sections of the receiver to perform their specific applications.

The classical method of describing this functional interrelationship pictorially is by the use of a block diagram (Fig. 1-1). However, a block diagram of an electronic system has only limited usefulness for instructional purposes. A block diagram is like an organization chart of a large corporation or a government agency; it reveals the principal and supporting functions. In addition, it shows which functions are of a controlling nature and which are subordinate. An organization chart *does not* reveal *how* these industrial functions are performed, any more than a block diagram of an electronic system reveals how the various individual electronic functions are performed. All of the books in this *Electronic Circuit Action Series* place great emphasis on explaining how the individual circuit actions are accomplished. The remaining chapters of this book are devoted to detailed analysis of circuit actions in the sections of the receiver depicted in Fig. 1-1.

THE TELEVISION SIGNAL

Fig. 1-2 shows some of the components of the typical television signal. The frequency-modulated (FM) sound carrier is shown in Fig. 1-2A. This signal has constant amplitude and varies around a center frequency near the high end of the frequency band allocated to that particular channel. The center frequency for the audio carrier is 5.75 mc above the low end of the band and .25 mc

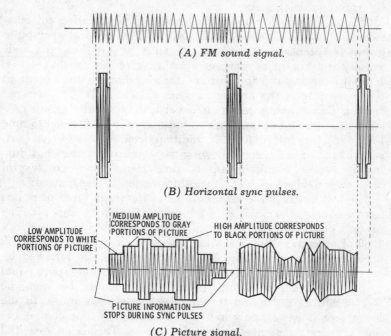

(A) FM sound signal.

(B) Horizontal sync pulses.

LOW AMPLITUDE CORRESPONDS TO WHITE PORTIONS OF PICTURE

MEDIUM AMPLITUDE CORRESPONDS TO GRAY PORTIONS OF PICTURE

HIGH AMPLITUDE CORRESPONDS TO BLACK PORTIONS OF PICTURE

PICTURE INFORMATION STOPS DURING SYNC PULSES

(C) Picture signal.

Fig. 1-2. Waveforms of the three types of intelligence which make up the composite video signal.

below the high end of the band. The maximum deviation permitted above and below the center frequency is 25 kc. The audio carrier is transmitted continuously, even in the absence of sound information.

Fig. 1-2B shows the horizontal synchronizing signals. These signals are used to pulse-modulate the picture carrier, and they occur at a rate of 15,750 pulses per second. Actually, three different types of pulses are used to pulse-modulate the carrier. The horizontal sync pulses are interrupted at regular intervals by additional pulses which are necessary to provide vertical synchronizing information to the receiver. These additional pulses consist of equalizing pulses and a series of wider pulses which are generally referred to collectively as the serrated vertical pulse.

Each horizontal pulse is superimposed on a somewhat wider base, called a blanking pedestal. The blanking-pedestal amplitude is made higher than the highest portion of the picture waveform; therefore it determines the "black level" of the video signal. The significance of this term is discussed more fully in Chapter 4. Each horizontal sync pulse indicates the start of a new line of picture information; thus, you would expect 15,750 such lines to be traced out each second.

The pulses which convey the vertical synchronizing information must occur 60 times each second. This vertical sync-pulse group is composed of six narrow equalizing pulses, six wide pulses, and six more narrow equalizing pulses in that order. If they were allowed to continue, these eighteen pulses occur at twice the rate of the horizontal sync pulses, or 31,500 times per second. Consequently, each such vertical sync-pulse group consumes the amount of time that would normally be devoted to nine lines of picture information. In addition, from nine to twelve horizontal sync pulses occur following the equalizing pulses but during the vertical blanking-pedestal time. Hence, there are several lines each field when no picture information is transmitted.

The width and phase relationships of the three types of pulses for two successive fields of a picture are given in Fig. 1-3. The process of integrating a vertical sync pulse begins once every 1/60 of a second when the wide pulses in the center of Fig. 1-3 occur. In each line of Fig. 1-3 the wide pulses are followed by six narrow equalizing pulses. In the upper line a wide space equal to one whole line of picture information is shown between the last equalizing pulse and the first horizontal sync pulse. In the lower line, however, only half of this amount of time elapses before the first horizontal sync pulse occurs. This is an essential part of the interlacing process, and it insures that the first line of one field will begin at the left edge of the screen, whereas the first line of the alternate field will begin in the center of the screen.

A new horizontal sync pulse occurs every 63.7 microseconds, since 15,750 of them occur every second. A single line of picture information lasts a somewhat shorter time, since each blanking pedestal consumes about 8 microseconds, and the picture line is not permitted to start until after the blanking pedestal has ended. One entire picture (known as a raster) is composed of 525 lines, and each raster is made up of two fields. Thus each field has 262.5 lines, and a new field is initiated every 1/60 of a second by a vertical sync pulse. The horizontal synchronizing action must continue even during the vertical synchronizing action to maintain horizontal synchronization. Alternate fields are interlaced

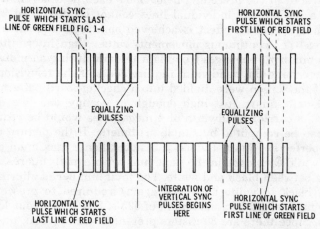

Fig. 1-3. Width and phase relationships of the three types of pulses in the composite video signal.

so that corresponding lines in successive fields are not overlaid on each other. Fig. 1-4 shows the manner in which the picture lines are interlaced between successive fields. Fig. 1-4 shows (solid blue) what the horizontal lines would look like during the vertical retrace period. We cannot see them, however, because they are blanked out during the entire vertical retrace action. In Fig. 1-4 the picture lines of the first field are shown in solid red. Interlaced between these red lines are the picture lines of the second field (solid green). Both sets of lines must slant slightly downward from left to right. Each such line takes about 55 microseconds to complete itself. The retrace action, which takes only about 1 or 2 microseconds, connects the end point of one picture line to the beginning of the next line; therefore, the retrace lines are essentially horizontal. These retrace lines are shown in dotted black. First, all the lines represented in red in Fig. 1-4 are traced. Then, after vertical retrace has occurred, the lines represented in green are traced.

The vertical retrace lines which follow the first (red) field are shown in dotted blue, and the vertical retrace lines which follow the second (green) field are shown in solid blue.

Fig. 1-2C shows two successive lines of picture information. Dark areas in the picture lead to maximum amplitude of the video voltage, and light areas cause minimum amplitude. The two lines of video voltage shown in this illustration would be part of a single field. On the next successive field, alternate lines would be illuminated by the scanning beam and interlaced between the lines traced in the preceding field. Since each field is renewed 60 times a second, the individual lines cannot be discerned by the human eye, and an effect is achieved similar to that in motion pictures—i.e., continuous movements rather than intermittent.

The number of changes from light to dark during an individual line determine the bandwidth requirements of the television carrier. If the screen were divided into a checkerboard pattern with each small square just high enough to occupy one line of the picture, a carrier bandwidth of 4 megacycles would be required. This can be computed by simple arithmetic. If the picture raster were perfectly square (which it is not), then a maximum of 525 lines would each contain the same number of small squares, alternating between black and white. The total number of alternations (from black to white and back again) required to present one entire field would be a maximum of $525 \times 525/2$, or about 137,800 cycles. Since there are 30 rasters presented each second, the total number of cycles per second would be $30 \times 137,800$, or about 4,130,000 cycles per second. The total number of individual picture elements, or squares, would be twice this figure, or about 8 million.

One important modification should be made to these calculations if one desires a more accurate figure. First, a television screen is not perfectly square. The width to height ratio, which is called the aspect ratio, is $4/3$. Therefore we would require four thirds as many squares in our checkerboard as were indicated previously. Also, since some lines are sacrificed during the vertical retrace period which follows each field, approximately eighteen lines are lost per raster. This does not significantly reduce the carrier bandwidth requirements, however, because during the approximately 55 microseconds which elapse during the scanning of each individual line, picture information will be occurring at the 4.13-mc rate calculated previously, after modification by

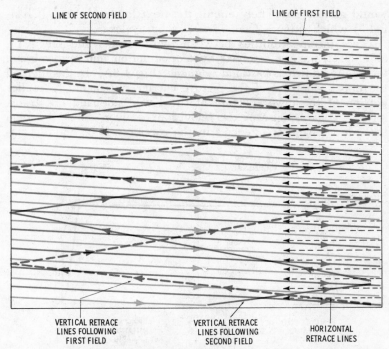

LINE OF SECOND FIELD   LINE OF FIRST FIELD

VERTICAL RETRACE   VERTICAL RETRACE
LINES FOLLOWING   LINES FOLLOWING   HORIZONTAL
FIRST FIELD   SECOND FIELD   RETRACE LINES

Fig. 1-4. Method of tracing a pattern on the TV screen.

the aspect ratio. This modification would raise the sideband requirement to 4/3 × 4.13, or about 5.4 megacycles.

This amount of sideband can occur on either side of the carrier frequency. Consequently, if double sideband modulation and transmission were used, almost 11 megacycles of bandwidth would be required to carry the picture information alone. The frequency-modulated sound carrier is allocated an additional 50 kilocycles of bandwidth. In addition, this FM band must be protected, or isolated, from the picture carrier by a minimum of 250 kilocycles, and it must also be isolated from the picture carrier of the next higher channel by the same amount (250 kc).

When all of these varied bandwidth requirements are added together, they become completely incompatible with the allowed 6-mc channel bandwidth. Fig. 1-5 shows a graphical relationship between these various requirements as applied to VHF Channel 6, (82 to 88 mc). The frequencies directly above 88 mc are not assigned for TV usage; they are allocated to other uses and cannot be encroached on. Therefore the position of the FM sound carrier is determined. It is evident that the double sideband carrier described previously would extend so far down in frequency that it would almost completely engulf the next lower channel (Channel 5) which extends from 76 to 82 megacycles.

These incompatibilities between requirements and the available spectrum are resolved by a modulation and transmission technique known as *vestigial sideband* (Fig. 1-6A). In this method the upper sideband of the picture carrier plus a much smaller portion of the lower portion of the lower sideband are transmitted. The response of the television receiver should be such that all sideband frequencies in the carrier will be equally am-

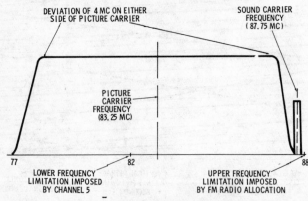

Fig. 1-5. Bandwidth requirements (Channel 6) if double-sideband transmission were employed.

plified. To accomplish this purpose, the receiver response curve should approximate that of Fig. 1-6B. The slope of the left edge of this response curve is arranged to pass through the zero point at the left edge of the channel; it also passes through the picture carrier (a center frequency) at the 50% response point. The picture carrier or center frequency is always located a distance of 1.25 mc below the low end of each channel; therefore, for Channel 6 it is located at 83.25 mc. The sloping portion of the response curve ends at 84.5 mc (1.25 mc above 83.25 mc).

An example of what happens to a video signal which differs from the picture carrier frequency by half a megacycle is shown in Fig. 1-6. Fig. 1-6A indicates that all of the upper sidebands and some of the lower sidebands of this signal are transmitted equally. Fig. 1-6B, however, indicates that 30% of the total amplification in the receiver will be from the lower sideband and 70% of the total amplification from the upper sideband.

An example of a video sideband which is 2 mc removed from the picture carrier is also given in Fig. 1-6. None of the lower sideband of this signal appears in the transmitter output of Fig.

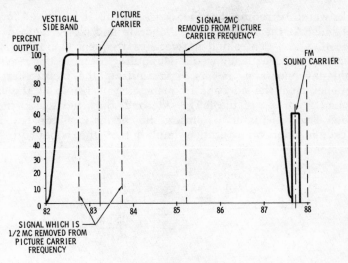

(A) Video signal.

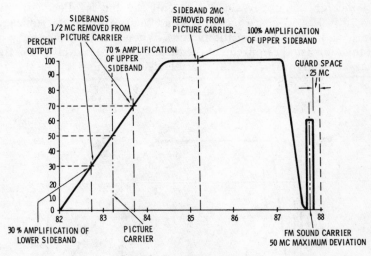

(B) Ideal receiver response.

Fig. 1-6. Bandwidth requirements (Channel 6) when vestigial-sideband transmission is employed.

1-6A. Within the receiver 100% of the total amplification of the signal is from the upper sideband.

Vestigial-sideband transmission offers several advantages over single-sideband transmission as the solution to the bandwidth requirements. If single sideband were used, very complex filter networks would be required at the transmitter to eliminate *all* lower sidebands. At the receiver end, elaborate and costly methods of generating and controlling a reference frequency equal to the picture-carrier frequency would be required, because the receiver would have no other means of recognizing the picture-carrier frequency from the sideband frequency. By transmitting the carrier and a portion of the lower sideband, the need for an independent local oscillator to reinsert the carrier is eliminated.

Vestigial-sideband operation implies that the bandwidth requirements are:

Lower sidebands	1.25 mc
Upper sidebands	5.40 mc
Guard spaces	.70 mc (approx.)
FM carrier	.05 mc
	7.40 mc

However, the modern receiver does not begin to use all of the bandwidth indicated by the computations. Instead of allowing 5.4 mc for the upper sidebands, only 4.0 mc is allocated; this amount of band space has proved adequate to provide sufficient clarity and definition in the picture. When this is done, the sum of the four listed requirements reduces to approximately 6 mc, the maximum allowable width of a television channel.

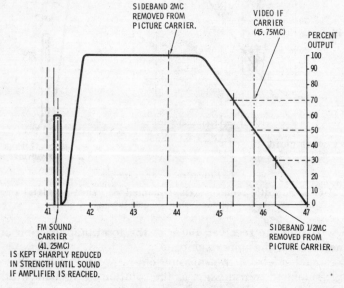

Fig. 1-7. Ideal video-IF response.

VIDEO IF SIGNAL

Typical circuits used to amplify the video IF signal that emerges from the tuner are discussed in a later chapter. The video-IF signal exhibits all of the significant characteristics of the original signal shown in Fig. 1-6B, except that these characteristics are occurring at a lower frequency. Fig. 1-7 shows the typical video IF signal. Another important difference between it and the original video signal is that the waveshape has been reversed. This occurs in the mixing process and results from the fact that the local-oscillator frequency is always *higher* than the incoming carrier frequency by the same fixed amount. The heterodyning process generates a difference frequency which is obtained by subtracting every signal component in the incoming video waveshape (picture carrier, sidebands, FM sound signal, etc.) from the local-oscillator frequency. This accounts for the fact that the FM sound carrier, which is at the high-frequency end of the video signal, is at the low-frequency end of the video IF signal.

REVIEW QUESTIONS

1. What is the bandwidth (in megacycles) allocated to a single television channel?

2. What is the width in megacycles of the channel spacing allocated to the sound signal in television transmission?

3. What is the width of the channel spacing (in megacycles) allocated to the picture or video information?

4. How many synchronizing pulses are transmitted during each second in the composite television signal? How far apart in time is each sync pulse?

5. How many fields per second are allowed by the composite television signal? How many individual lines are there per field? How many individual lines are lost, or masked, during each field by the time given to the synchronizing pulses?

6. What is the relationship between a raster and a field?

7. Define "aspect ratio." What is the physiological reason which makes the aspect ratio important?

Chapter 2

RF AMPLIFIER CIRCUITS

The term *tuners* in television is commonly taken to mean those circuits at the "front end" of a receiver through which the received signal must be processed before it passes into the various amplifying portions of the receiver. In all modern receivers these front-end circuits include some provision for initial amplification of the received RF signal, generating an entirely separate oscillator frequency and combining, or mixing, these two frequencies so as to generate a third new frequency. The resultant frequency is known as the intermediate frequency, or IF. To accomplish these basic functions, the typical tuner includes three individual tube circuits: a radio-frequency (RF) amplifier stage, an oscillator stage, and a mixer stage. This chapter is devoted to the RF amplifier stage; the oscillator and mixer stages are discussed in Chapter 3.

CASCODE RF AMPLIFIER

Figs. 2-1 and 2-2 depict two separate moments in the operation of a typical RF amplifier circuit. This tuning system uses the "incremental inductance" method, whereby channels are changed by adding or removing some inductance to the tuned circuits that determine the operating frequency of the stage. Two of the inductors are shown in Figs. 2-1 and 2-2. They are:

1. Coils L7 through L12 and L14 through L17, situated between the antenna input circuit and the grid of the first RF amplifier (V1A).
2. Coils L20 through L25 and L27 through L30, in the plate circuit of the second RF amplifier (V1B).

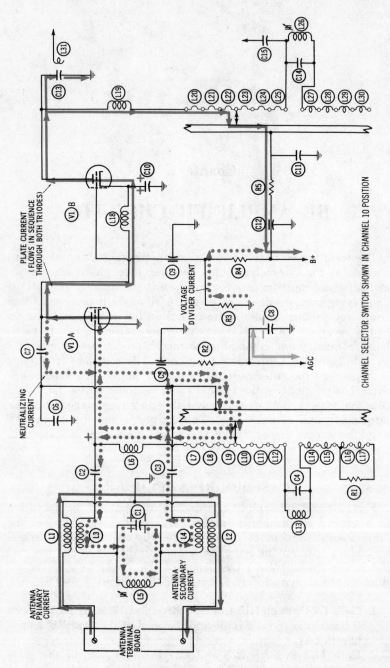

Fig. 2-1. Operation of a cascode RF amplifier tuned to Channel 10.

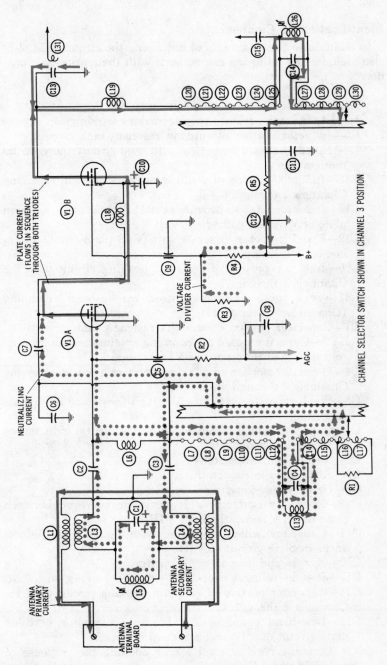

Fig. 2-2. Operation of a cascode RF amplifier tuned to Channel 3.

Identification of Components

In addition to these two sets of inductors, the circuit (Fig. 2-1) also includes the following components with their principal functions.

L1, L2—Antenna transformer primary windings.

L3, L4—Antenna transformer secondary windings.

L5—Inductor portion of antenna resonant tank circuit.

L6—Fixed inductor in series with grid-circuit incremental inductances.

L13—Inductor portion of peaking network used in receiving Channels 2 through 6.

L18—Inductor used to provide partial degeneration between plate of V1A and cathode of V1B.

L19—Fixed inductor in series with V1B plate-circuit incremental inductances.

L26—Inductor portion of resonant peaking circuit used for Channels 2 through 6.

L31—Very small inductance used in "hi-band" coupling (Channels 7 through 13).

C1—Capacitor portion of antenna resonant tank circuit.

C2, C3—Capacitors used for coupling antenna secondary current into the grid circuit of V1A.

C4—Capacitor portion of peaking network used in receiving Channels 2 through 6.

C5—Small capacitance to ground (high-frequency RF bypass capacitor).

C6—Capacitor which resonates with incremental inductances in V1A grid circuit.

C7—Neutralizing capacitor.

C8—AGC storage capacitor.

C9—Grid bypass capacitor.

C10—Capacitor used to provide partial degeneration between plate of V1A and cathode of V1B.

C11—Capacitor which resonates with incremental inductances in plate circuit of V1B.

C12—Bypass and decoupling capacitor.

C13—Part of hi-band coupling "gimmick," along with L31.

C14—Capacitor portion of resonant peaking circuit used for Channels 2 through 6.

C15—Low-band coupling and blocking capacitor between plate circuit of V1B and mixer grid circuit.

R1—Damping resistor used for broadening the response of coils L16 and L17.

R2—Isolating resistor between V1A grid and AGC circuit.

R3, R4—Voltage-dividing network used to provide high positive voltage at grid of V1B.

R5—Decoupling resistor between plate circuit of V1B and B+ power source.

V1—Dual-triode RF amplifier tube.

Identification of Currents

Several different electron currents are flowing through the various components in the circuit of Figs. 2-1 and 2-2. Many of these currents follow intricate and sometimes obscure paths while performing their necessary functions; however, there are no unnecessary functions performed. Since each electron current is performing one or more necessary functions, it is mandatory to be able to visualize each one of the following currents at work in the circuit.

1. Antenna transformer primary current (solid blue).
2. Antenna transformer secondary current (dotted blue).
3. Plate current through V1A and V1B (solid red).
4. Neutralizing current between plate and grid of V1A (dotted red).
5. Voltage-divider current through R3 and R4 (also in dotted red).
6. Automatic gain control (AGC) current (solid green).

Details of Operation

The antenna transformer consists of the two primary windings (L1 and L2) and the two secondary windings (L3 and L4). The two primary windings connect directly to the twin leads of the familiar 300-ohm television lead-in cable so that signals induced in the antenna will flow in opposite directions through L1 and L2. Fig. 2-1 shows this antenna current (solid blue) flowing to the right through L1 toward the ground connection, while the same current flows to the left through L2 away from the ground connection. These currents induce the secondary currents (dotted blue) flowing to the left through L3 and to the right through L4. These secondary currents reinforce each other and drive the current shown in dotted blue through inductor L6 and whatever portion of the incremental inductances that are connected in the circuit. It should be understood that the direction of flow shown in Fig. 2-1 persists for only half of a cycle of the radio frequency. At the end of each half-cycle the antenna primary current and the resulting secondary current reverse in direction. Since the frequency of the high-band VHF channels (7 through 13) extends from 174 to 216 mc, it is evident that these reversals must occur hundreds of millions of times *each second.*

The complete flow-path of the antenna secondary current during the half-cycle shown in Fig. 2-1 is upward through incremental inductances L9, L8, and L7, then through L6 and onto the right-hand plate of coupling capacitor C2. From C2 the path continues through L3, L5, and L4 and onto the left-hand plate of C3. The path from C3 is completed downward through the shorting bar of the rotary switch to the point where it makes contact with the incremental inductances.

All of the components listed in the preceding paragraph, along with C1 and C6, constitute a complex tuned circuit. The purpose of this circuit is to form a resonant circuit at the frequency selected by the channel selector. Thus, the received signal can be built up to its maximum possible strength prior to amplification by the RF amplifiers. This condition of resonance is supported by the movements of the antenna primary current back and forth through L1 and L2. These current movements induce the necessary supporting currents in L3 and L4. The preceding induction process goes on continuously throughout each entire cycle of antenna primary current. The net result of this resonant current flow is the appearance (at the upper terminal of L6) of alternate negative and positive voltage peaks which "drive" the control grid of V1A.

Neutralizing Circuit Action

The neutralizing current (dotted red) flows between the left plate of C7 and the control grid of V1A, flowing upward through the incremental inductances and L6. This current is driven by the fluctuations in plate current through V1A. Its purpose, or function, is to prevent the grid circuit of V1A from breaking into self-sustained oscillations. A triode amplifier with a tuned-grid circuit must always be considered susceptible to oscillation, because the necessary feedback action (that indispensable element of any self-sustained oscillation) between output and input circuits can occur between plate and grid of the tube. (Within the tube the coupling is via the interelectrode capacitance between the plate and grid.)

This feedback action would work in the following manner. When the grid of V1A is made positive by the antenna secondary current (Fig. 2-1), the plate current through the tube is increased. This increase in plate current delivers electrons into the plate area and lowers the plate voltage. The reduction in plate voltage is "sensed" by the orbiting electrons within the metal structure of the control grid located only a few millimeters away. Some of these orbiting electrons within the grid structure are dislodged from their planetary orbits by this drop in plate voltage, and they are driven away from the grid element into its external circuit. This action creates a slight *additional* electron deficiency at the control grid, producing what amounts to a self-induced component of positive voltage.

This additional component of positive voltage causes a further increase in the plate-current stream and an additional reduction in plate voltage. During the negative half-cycles (one of which is depicted by Fig. 2-2), the flow direction of the antenna secondary current makes the control grid of V1A negative. This negative control-grid voltage reduces the quantity of electrons flowing in the plate-current stream through the tube, causing a rise in the plate voltage. Some orbiting electrons in the metal structure of the control grid will be drawn out of their orbits and assembled on the portions of the grid closest to the plate of the tube because of this rise in plate voltage.

These two actions are fundamentally what would happen if the plate and grid were two opposing plates of a capacitor. When the voltage at one capacitor plate is alternately lowered and raised by some means, electrons must alternately flow out of or onto the other plate in response to this action.

When the grid is connected to a tuned circuit, as is the case here, this feedback action can lead to sustained oscillation, because each such feedback impulse excites and replenishes a corresponding half-cycle of current movement in the tuned circuit. Thus, a current resembling the antenna secondary current and flowing along the same path can be excited into oscillation, even though no such similar signal is being received by the antenna.

The function of the neutralizing capacitor and the neutralizing current is to counteract this undesirable chain of events and, in fact, keep it from occurring. C7 is the neutralizing capacitor; it is chosen to have approximately the same value as the interelectrode capacitance of the tube. C7 connects the plate of the tube to the end of the tuned tank circuit opposite the grid. Consequently, whenever the plate voltage is changed in any way (either raised or lowered), equal impulses of current are simultaneously withdrawn from or delivered to opposite ends of the tuned circuit. Thus, while one such impulse might excite the tuned circuit to oscillation, the other impulse will have exactly the opposite effect and will tend to dampen out or oppose any tendency of the tuned circuit to oscillate.

Fig. 2-1 shows this neutralizing current (dotted red) being driven to the left through C7 to the far end of the tuned circuit. This action occurs when the plate-current stream is pouring additional electrons into the plate area, thereby lowering the plate voltage. At this same moment the undesired feedback action is driving approximately an equal number of electrons away from the control grid and into the top of the tuned circuit. Thus, the two currents counteract, or "neutralize," each other.

Fig. 2-2 shows the neutralizing current (again in dotted red) being drawn away from the bottom of the tuned circuit and onto the left-hand plate of C7. This occurs at the moment when the plate-current stream has been reduced in value and is delivering fewer electrons to the plate area. At the same time, the inter-electrode feedback action is drawing an equal-sized electron current away from the top of the tuned-tank circuit and toward the grid. Again, the two plate-to-grid feedback actions neutralize each other, and the tuned grid circuit is prevented from breaking into self-sustained oscillations.

Amplifier Operation

V1 is a dual triode tube whose respective halves are in a *cascode* arrangement. The term *cascode amplifier* identifies a circuit in which the plate of one tube is connected directly to the cathode of the next succeeding stage. This arrangement requires that the plate current of the first tube must also flow as plate current through the *second* tube. This feature is illustrated by the plate current lines (solid red) in Figs. 2-1 and 2-2.

The plate of V2B is connected to the B+ source through L19, the portion of the incremental inductances connected between L19 and the rotary switch shorting bar and decoupling resistor R5. The B+ voltage in an arrangement of this nature will be on the order of 230 volts. This positive voltage draws electron current across the tube (V1B) from cathode to plate. The departure of emitted electrons from the cathode creates a positive voltage (of lesser value) at the cathode of V1B. This positive voltage is indicated by plus signs on the upper plate of capacitor C10; it is this voltage that is applied to the plate of V1A and draws electron current across this tube. Since V1A and V1B are probably identical triodes, representing equal amounts of equivalent resistance to the flow of plate currents, the tubes will "drop" equal amounts of the total applied voltage, or about 115 volts each. Thus the voltage on C10 will be about +115 volts. The complete path of the plate current begins at ground below the cathode of V1A. It flows through V1A, L18, V1B, L19, some portion of the incremental coils (L20, L21, and L22 in Fig. 2-1), and R5 before reaching the power supply.

Each of the triodes functions as an RF amplifier; consequently, we must expect the plate current to fluctuate, or pulsate. Whenever the grid of V1A is made positive by the movements of the antenna secondary current through inductor L6, the plate-current stream through V1A will be increased in quantity. This action delivers additional electrons through L18 to the top of C10 and the cathode of V1B; this, in effect, lowers the cathode voltage of the second tube. V2B is, in actuality, a cathode-driven amplifier; its control grid is held at a fixed voltage determined by the voltage-divider current (dotted red) flowing upward through R3 and downward through R4 to the power supply.

Since these are equal-valued resistors (470,000 ohms each), the voltage at their junction and at the control grid of V1A will also be approximately +115 volts—the same as the average voltage applied to the cathode. Thus, a condition of "zero grid bias" exists for the second amplifier tube (meaning zero voltage difference between grid and cathode). When the plate current through V1A increases, the cathode voltage of V1B will be decreased. This amounts to applying a positive voltage to the grid of V1B so that the plate current through tube V1B is simultaneously increased.

On the next succeeding half-cycle (shown in Fig. 2-2). the antenna primary and secondary currents will both reverse their directions, and the voltage at the grid of V1A will be made *more* negative. This more negative grid voltage will restrict, or reduce, the flow of electrons (plate current) through V1A; thus, fewer electrons will be delivered to the cathode area of V1B. This amounts to a small rise in the positive voltage at this cathode and causes a reduction in the plate current through V1B.

It is a characteristic of a triode amplifier tube that a small change in the voltage difference between its grid and cathode will produce a relatively large change in the amount of plate current flowing through the tube. Therefore, the relatively large changes in plate current through V1A are converted into a much larger cycle of alternating voltage on the upper plate of C10. The alternating voltage that appears on C10 is the output voltage of V1A; it will normally be many times greater than the alternating voltage (input) applied to the grid of V1A.

The alternating voltage on C10 becomes the driving voltage for V1B and results in much larger pulsations of plate current through V1B than are flowing through V1A. This cannot mean that *more* plate current flows through V1B than through V1A, because the two plate currents must be equal from cycle to cycle. One way of describing it is to say that when the current through V1A increases, the current through V1B increases even more, and when the current through V1A decreases, the current through V1B decreases even more.

27

These greater fluctuations in plate current through V1B generate greater voltage swings in the plate-load circuit consisting of C13 paralleled with inductor L19 and the incremental inductances. This load circuit is a tuned tank that will resonate across the entire bandwidth of the particular channel being received. This condition of resonance is supported, or sustained, by the pulsations in plate current as they flow into the inductors. The resulting tank voltage is coupled to the grid circuit of the mixer stage by one of two methods. For the high channels a device known as "gimmick coupling" is used. This gimmick is a very small amount of inductance (labeled L31 in Figs. 2-1 and 2-2) consisting of a turn or two of insulated wire wrapped around the lead of C13. For the low channels coupling is via capacitor C15. Operation of the mixer stage is discussed in Chapter 3.

Inductance and Capacitance

All of the tuner circuitry, which includes the RF amplifier and the oscillator and mixer circuits discussed in Chapter 3, is normally housed in a small sheltered section of the receiver. Therefore it is not easily maintained. Tuner maintenance is, in fact, a specialty which the inexperienced should not attempt. It is not a good idea to do any random probing of the various inductances and capacitances that determine the resonant frequencies of the tuned circuits. Because of the very high frequencies of current involved, the intrinsic values of the inductances and capacitances are very small. Any slight change in the distributed inductance of any of the incremental coils can make an unacceptably large change in the total inductance of the tuned circuit. Likewise, any slight change in the inherent capacitance to ground of the various tuner components can significantly alter the total circuit capacitance and thereby alter the resonant frequency of the circuit.

As an example of the small circuit values involved, apply the standard frequency formula to the center frequency of Channel 10 (195 mc). If we provide 10 micromicrofarads of capacitance across the inductances of the grid tank circuit of the RF amplifier (V1A), we have the following values:

$$f = \frac{1}{2\pi\sqrt{LC}}$$

therefore,

$$L = \frac{1}{4\pi^2 f^2 C}$$

where,

    f is the resonant frequency in cycles per second,
    L is the inductance in henrys,
    C is the capacitance in farads.

Solving for the values listed previously:

$$L = \frac{1}{39.4 \times 195 \times 195 \times 10^{12} \times 10 \times 10^{-12}}$$

$$= \frac{1}{39.4 \times 38,025 \times 10}$$

$$= \frac{1}{39.4 \times 38.025 \times 10^3}$$

$$= \frac{1}{1,498,185 \times 10}$$

$$= .000000066 \text{ henry}$$

$$= .066 \text{ microhenry}$$

This is an extremely small amount of inductance (hardly more than one or two turns of carefully wound wire around an air core), and yet it will resonate with 10 micromicrofarads of capacitance at the center frequency of Channel 10.

As was pointed out in Chapter 1, the first five TV channels are separated from the next seven by a band of frequencies nearly 100 mc wide. Channel 6 must receive signals from 82 to 88 mc, while Channel 7 must receive signals from 174 to 180 mc. Because of this frequency separation, considerably more inductance and capacitance are required to tune the five low channels than are required by the next seven channels. In the RF-amplifier grid circuit these additional circuit values are provided by L13 and C4. Since L13 is in series between the upper and lower portions of the total incremental inductance windings (L7 to L12 and L14 to L17), the grid tank current must flow up and down through L13 whenever any of the lower inductances are cut into the circuit. L13 is the additional amount of inductance necessary to switch the grid tank circuit from a condition of resonance at Channel 7 to resonance at Channel 6. C4 is the additional capacitance necessary for the same purpose.

Inspection of the frequency formula might indicate that the capacitance could be left constant and the resonant frequency lowered by greater additions of incremental inductance. Theoretically this is possible because the frequency varies inversely to the square root of either the inductance or capacitance. Practically speaking, however, it is not desirable because the quality, or "sharpness," of resonance of any tuned circuit varies directly with the amount of inductance in the circuit. The formula which relates these factors is:

$$Q = \frac{2\pi fL}{R}$$

where,

    Q is the quality,
    f is the circuit frequency in cps,
    L is the total circuit inductance in henrys,
    R is the total circuit resistance in ohms.

Often sharpness of resonance is desirable, but not when receiving a television channel signal 6 mc wide. A broadband, uniform or equal response to any frequency within the desired band is preferred.

R1, which is placed in parallel with the two lowest incremental inductances (L16 and L17), represents a classical method of broadening, or increasing, the width of a band by reducing the response. When L17 is connected into the grid tank circuit, as it is when Channel 2 is being received, some portion of the tank current will be diverted from L16 and L17 and will flow up and down through this resistor instead. Essentially, the resistor has the same effect as decreasing the total circuit inductance through which all of the tank current flows. The foregoing formula indicates a commensurate decrease in the circuit quality (Q).

The higher-valued resistors will have the least effect in widening the bandwidth, because they permit smaller quantities of tank current to be diverted from the inductors. Low-value resistors, such as R1, will divert more of this current. As more current is diverted through the resistor, the sharpness at resonance will be decreased, and the bandwidth, when tuned to Channel 2, will be increased.

C14, in parallel with L26 in the plate-tank circuit of the RF amplifier, provides additional capacitance to a resonant circuit to facilitate tuning the lower frequencies of Channels 2 through 6. The addition of this capacitor produces the desirable effect of reducing the amount of circuit inductance required to make the circuit resonant. Thus, the capacitor contributes to a reduction in circuit quality, with the same resultant increase in bandwidth of the circuit.

AGC Circuitry

Nothing has yet been said about the AGC voltage which biases the control grid of the first RF amplifier tube (V1A). The AGC voltage is an accumulation of electrons on the upper plate of C8 (indicated by the green minus signs). Since the control grid of V1A is connected to this point, the intrinsic amount of this voltage at any instant has a direct effect on the quantity of plate current that can flow through V1A. Consequently, the amplification or gain which can be realized from this tube will be affected.

The AGC voltage is fed by the AGC current (solid green). The AGC current reaches this point by flowing through a very large (1 megohm or larger) resistor (not shown in the diagrams). This current comes from the plate current of an AGC tube, which conducts once during each sync pulse. When the AGC tube conducts, the AGC current shown in Figs. 2-1 and 2-2 flows up and toward the right, delivering additional electrons into the storage on the upper plate of C8. When the AGC tube is not conducting, this current flows to the left and downward, draining some electrons away from C8. These two processes may be described as "charging" and "discharging" actions, respectively.

If the received signal increases in strength due to propagation anomalies, the sync pulses will also increase in strength, and the amount of plate current conducted by the AGC tube each cycle will increase. As a result, *additional* electrons will be delivered to the upper plate of C8, and the amount of the negative AGC voltage will increase proportionately. Since this voltage is applied to the control grid of V1A, an increase in signal strength reduces the amount of current allowed to flow through the tubes; consequently, the amplification, or gain, of the tube is reduced.

The complete story of circuit actions associated with the development of an AGC voltage is given in detail in the companion volume, *TV Sync and Deflection Circuit Actions.*

Tuning to Lower Channels

Fig. 2-2 depicts some of the significant current-flow patterns through this same tuner when it is tuned to one of the lower channels—in this case, Channel 3. The frequency limits for this channel are 60 to 66 mc; therefore, considerably more capacitance and/or inductance must be incorporated in the tuned circuits in order to resonate at the lower frequencies. In Fig. 2-2, the selector switch (rotary switch) for the incremental inductances has been moved so as to include more of these circuit constants in the path of the resonant current. Thus, in the grid tank circuit of V1A the antenna secondary current (solid blue) is flowing through coils L7 to L16. Also, an extra capacitor (C4) is included in this circuit. The neutralizing current (dotted red) must also flow through all these inductors.

In the plate-tank circuit of V1B, incremental coils L20 through L29 are now part of the plate circuit. The plate current from the amplifier flows downward through all of these coils as well as through L26 in order to reach the shorting bar of the rotary switch. From here it flows through R5 to the power supply.

In Fig. 2-2 the alternating currents are shown flowing in opposite directions from that shown in Fig. 2-1. These currents include the two tank currents, the antenna currents, and the neutralizing current. It is not as easy to portray increases or decreases in quantity of the one-way currents which are known as pulsating direct currents, such as the tube plate currents. It should be understood that while this current always flows in the direction indicated, the actual *amount* of flow is constantly changing in step with the applied signal.

TETRODE RF AMPLIFIER

A tetrode RF-amplifier circuit employed in a tuner which uses separate tuning circuits for each channel is given in Fig. 2-3. In this tuner, separate coils for each tuned circuit are mounted on a drum or turret assembly. When the channel-selector switch is rotated to a given channel, the proper coils to tune that particular channel are inserted in the circuit. This method and the incremental-inductance method of tuning (depicted earlier) are the two most popular systems employed in modern TV receivers.

Identification of Components

This tuner is composed of the following components which perform the functions indicated:

L1, L2—Antenna transformer primary windings.
L3, L4—Antenna transformer secondary windings.
L5, L6, L7—Filter coils.
L8—Inductor used to achieve resonance in grid circuit.
L9—Inductance component of amplifier plate circuit.
L10—Inductance component of mixer grid circuit.
C1, C2—Input coupling capacitors.
C3, C4, C5, C6, C8—Filter capacitors in input network.
C7—Input coupling capacitor.
C9—AGC storage capacitor.
C10—Part of resonant tank in RF amplifier plate circuit.
C11—Screen-grid filter capacitor.
C12—Plate-tank decoupling capacitor.
C13—Part of resonant tank leading to mixer grid.
R1, R2—Part of antenna input network.
R3—Grid-driving resistor for RF amplifier.
R4—Decoupling resistor.
V1—2FS5 RF tetrode amplifier.

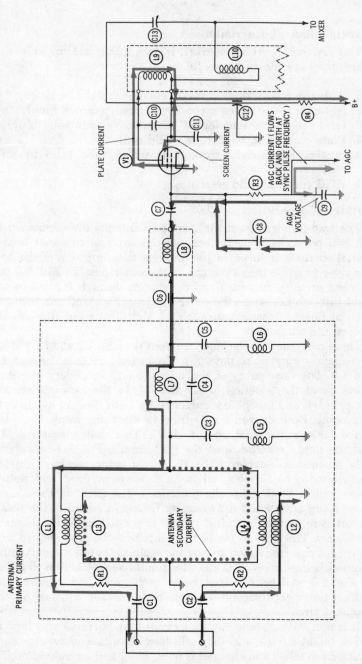

Fig. 2-3. Operation of a tetrode RF amplifier circuit.

33

Identification of Currents

The electron currents at work in this tuner and the colors in which they are shown are as follows:

1. Antenna transformer primary current (solid blue).
2. Antenna transformer secondary current (dotted blue).
3. Grid-driving current for RF amplifier (also in solid blue).
4. Plate current through tube (solid red).
5. Screen-grid current through amplifier tube (also in solid red).
6. AGC current (solid green).

Details of Operation

The lead-in wires from the television antenna are connected to the two points at opposite ends of the antenna terminal board. Signal currents induced in the antenna flow *into* one of the terminal posts while they flow out of the other post. In Fig. 2-3 the antenna primary current flows downward through R2 and to the right through L2, while the other portion of the antenna primary current flows to the left through L1 and downward through R1 toward the antenna.

These movements of primary current through L1 and L2 induce a secondary current to flow in a clockwise direction through L4 and L3. The flow paths of the primary and secondary currents converge at the junction of L1 and L4. In the example shown, the primary and secondary currents are both flowing *away* from this point. Both currents are drawing electrons away from the tuned tank in the grid circuit of V1. This tank consists of L8 and the total capacitance of the grid circuit. Fig. 2-3 represents only a single half-cycle of the TV signal being received; during the alternate half-cycles, all flows (shown in solid and dotted blue) will be in the opposite directions. The effect of these electrons being alternately drawn away from and added to the tuned circuit is to excite the tuned tank into oscillation at its resonant frequency. The sizes of the components have been chosen so that their resonant frequency will be the same as that of the particular channel being received. Thus, the reinforcement action depicted in Fig. 2-3 will be repeated twice each cycle and hundreds of million times each second. A large tank current will flow in the resonant circuit.

It is more accurate to say that *many* tank currents will flow in the resonant circuit, and they will flow simultaneously with each other. Each television channel is 6 mc wide, and an individual TV signal is a complex of many frequencies. The audio frequencies which are modulated on the upper end of each channel band are occurring continuously. Human speech and music are almost never represented by a single pitch or frequency; they are a combination of many sounds occurring in unison. Each such sound is represented by a different audio frequency, with the result that the sound signal being received on any channel consists of several frequencies centered around the sound carrier. The picture-carrier frequency is centered 1.25 mc above the lower end of the band, but at any instant the picture frequency may be anywhere within the 4.5-mc portion of the channel allocated to the picture.

The tuned circuit must be "broadband" enough to accept any and all of these picture and sound frequencies and to let them build up to approximately equal strength. All of the inductive and capacitive components shown in the input circuit contribute to this broadbanding process in some way, but it is impossible to draw a meaningful picture of all the current actions which must occur throughout all of these components. The series circuits which lead to ground from either side of the tank circuit (C3-L5 and C5-L6) are tuned to particular frequency bands which must be eliminated. Two of the most obvious examples of frequencies which must be eliminated are the band between 40 and 50 mc and the band between 88 and 174 mc. Since the video IF of most modern TV receivers extends from 41 to 47 mc, any signals at these frequencies could be coupled through the tuner and onto the IF amplifiers where they would be amplified the same as any other signal. This band is used by many government and public service agencies and by many commercial establishments. Another possible source of signals in this region is the radiation of video IF signals from one TV set to another. The band between 88 and 174 mc, which separates Channels 6 and 7, is also used by many services. Commercial FM radio employs the band from 88 to 108 mc. Other users of this band include airline communications, navigational aids, government agencies, amateur radio, and others.

C3 and L5 represent the classical configuration of a series-resonant circuit which always presents a very low impedance to currents at its resonant frequency. As an example, suppose that these two components are chosen so as to be resonant in the vicinity of 90 mc at the low end of the FM radio band. FM signals at or near this frequency might get through the RF amplifier, be further amplified before demodulation, and eventually be heard as a competing sound signal when Channel 6 is being received. A series-resonant circuit leading to ground will act as a "short circuit" to all currents at its resonant frequency, effectively diverting them from the unwanted path and bypassing them to ground. The values of C5 and L6 might be chosen to resonate at some other offending frequency—for example, one close to 174 mc or in the 40-mc region. A series-resonant circuit with properly chosen components can be made to divert any offensive currents harmlessly to ground.

L7 and C4 represent a classical case of a parallel-resonant circuit being used to block the passage of a particular frequency or band of frequencies. A parallel-resonant circuit is said to present a *high impedance* to the passage of currents at its resonant frequency. The capacitor and inductor could be chosen to resonate at one of the same frequencies being bypassed to ground by the series-resonant circuits just discussed. Thus, while the parallel resonant circuit is blocking the passage of such a frequency, the series resonant circuit will be diverting it to ground. However, the components of the parallel-resonant circuit may be chosen to block another band of offensive frequencies.

L8 is shown enclosed in dashed lines. This identifies it as a component which is changed as the selector switch moves from one channel to another. Thus L8 makes a definite contribution to the resonant frequency of the entire grid circuit; it resonates with the total capacitance of the grid circuit at the frequency band assigned to the particular channel.

The grid-driving current (solid blue) flows up and down through grid resistor R3. In doing so, an RF voltage is developed at the amplifier grid. As this current flows downward through the resistor, it develops a negative voltage at the upper terminal. When it flows upward (as in Fig. 2-3), it develops a positive voltage. The amount of this current is very slight so that the quantity of electrons which it alternately delivers to or withdraws from the upper plate of the AGC capacitor (C9) will not appreciably change the AGC voltage stored there. The AGC voltage is indicated by the green minus signs on the upper plate. Since C9 is a very large capacitor, it requires a great many electrons in storage to create the few negative volts which constitute the AGC voltage. This voltage is supplied by the AGC current (solid green) which flows back and forth at the sync-pulse frequency. The AGC voltage provides the initial biasing voltage for the grid of the amplifier tube; this initial voltage is varied at a radio-frequency rate by the movements of the signal current up and down through R3.

The plate current (solid red) flows continuously through the tube, although its *quantity* is fluctuating or varying between wide limits as a result of the voltage changes at the grid. When tube current flows continuously in this manner, it is defined as Class-A operation. The complete path of this current takes it through the tube and down through L9 and R4 toward the power supply. L9 is

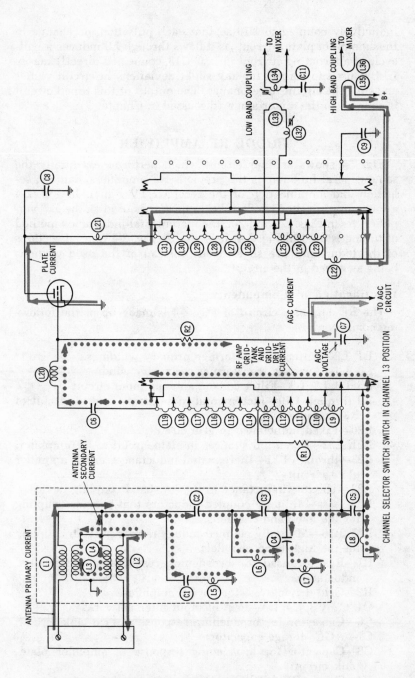

Fig. 2-4. Operation of a triode RF-amplifier circuit.

inductively coupled to L10 so that each pulsation, or change in the amount of plate current, as it flows through L9 induces a half-cycle of alternating current in L10. C13, connected directly across L10, is used to correct for any slight deviations in circuit values and tune the circuit to resonance. The output of this tuned circuit is coupled to the mixer stage (discussed in Chapter 3).

TRIODE RF AMPLIFIER

Fig. 2-4 shows another circuit which performs essentially the same general function as the previous RF amplifiers, namely, selection and amplification of the received TV signal. In Fig. 2-4 a low-noise nuvistor triode tube (a 6CW4) is used as the RF amplifier. As in Figs. 2-1 and 2-2, the incremental-inductance method of tuning is used in Fig. 2-4; however, in Fig. 2-4 unused sections of the inductance are shorted out, instead of the used portions being switched in the circuit.

Identification of Components

The RF-amplifier circuit of Fig. 2-4 is made up of the following components:

L1, L2—Antenna transformer primary windings.

L3, L4—Antenna transformer secondary windings.

L5, L6, L7, L8—Filter coils in antenna input circuit.

L9 through L19—Incremental inductances in grid circuit of RF amplifier.

L20—Fixed inductance in grid circuit.

L21, L22—Fixed inductances in plate circuit of RF amplifier.

L23—through L31—Incremental inductances in RF amplifier plate circuit.

L32—Tunable inductance in the low-band coupling device.

L33, L34—Mutually coupled inductors that provide coupling for the low-band channels.

L35, L36—Mutually coupled inductors that provide coupling for the high-band channels.

R1—Resistor used for broadening response of incremental inductances.

R2—Grid-driving resistor for RF amplifier.

C1, C2, C3, C4, C5—Part of input filter network.

C6—Capacitor for broadening response of grid-tank circuit.

C7—AGC storage capacitor.

C8—Capacitor for broadening response of amplifier plate-tank circuit.

V1—Triode RF amplifier tube.

Identification of Currents

The electron currents which flow in this circuit and the colors in which they are shown are as follows:

1. Antenna transformer primary current (solid blue).
2. Antenna transformer secondary current (dotted blue).
3. Grid-tank and grid-driving current (also in dotted blue).
4. Plate current (solid red).
5. AGC current (solid green).

Details of Operation

Operation of the circuit in Fig. 2-4 is essentially the same as for the previous circuits. The two leads on the antenna terminal board are connected to the twin lead-in wire from the television antenna. A signal induced in the antenna will drive electron current back and forth in the transformer primary windings (L1 and L2). At the instant depicted by Fig. 2-4, the primary current is being driven to the right through L1 and to the left through L2. A half-cycle later these flow directions are reversed. These primary currents induce secondary currents in inductors L3 and L4; in Fig. 2-4 the secondary currents are flowing in a counterclockwise direction. These currents reinforce each other, joining up with the primary current at the right-hand terminal of L4. Both of these currents then drive electrons up and down through the elaborate filter network which includes C1 through C5 and L5 through L8. In Fig. 2-4 this current is moving downward. Capacitor C5 in this network is also paralleled with the incremental inductances so that they have a natural tendency to resonate at some frequency and to build up an oscillation of electrons between the inductance and capacitance. The particular frequency at which this oscillation occurs is determined by the amount of inductance and capacitance in the circuit.

Resistor R1 diverts some portion of the tank current which would otherwise flow through the incremental inductances. This has the expected dual effect of weakening the strength of the oscillating current in this tank and also broadening, or widening, the response curve so it passes the entire 6-mc band with about equal strength. As the shorting bar moves downward from its uppermost point (Channel 13), the amount of inductance (and inductive reactance) increases.

The oscillation of electrons in this grid tank drives an electron current in and out of C6 and up and down through L20 and R2. This alternating current movement up and down through R2 develops the alternating voltage at the upper terminal of R2, which becomes the grid-driving voltage. This driving voltage acts as a throttle valve on the electron stream flowing through the tube, causing it to fluctuate, or pulsate, at the signal frequency. This current (solid red) is the tube-plate current. It carries these pulsations into the plate-load inductors and excites a condition of resonance between these inductors and tank capacitor C8.

The relationship between the shorting-bar position and the two coupling devices is an interesting one. With the shorting bar in the position shown, the low-band coupling device made up of L32, L33, and L34 is short-circuited so that it is not included in the circuit. However, the high-band coupling device consisting of L35 and L36 is in the circuit so that the plate-tank current flows through L35 at all times and induces a companion current in L36. When the shorting bar passes L33 (when tuning from Channel 7 to Channel 6), the low-band coupling circuits (L33 and L34) are connected in the circuit. Thus, for the high bands, coupling to the mixer stage is via L35 and L36; for the low bands L35 and L36 remain in the circuit, but L33 and L34 are also added.

REVIEW QUESTIONS

1. What is the distinguishing feature of the dual-triode circuit, regarding the plate current?

2. What important function is performed by the neutralizing current in the cascode amplifier?

3. What function is performed by the voltage divider current through R3 and R4 in Figs. 2-1 and 2-2?

4. If the sync pulses increase in strength due to propagation anomalies, what happens to the negative voltage on the upper plate of C8 in Figs. 2-1 and 2-2? What is the negative voltage on the capacitor called? What effect does it have on the operation of V1A?

5. To what uses and users is the frequency band of 88 to 108 megacycles allocated?

6. What two important functions are usually performed by RF amplifiers?

Chapter 3

OSCILLATOR AND
MIXER CIRCUITS

As stated in Chapter 2, three essential functions are performed in the tuner of modern TV receivers. The first of these functions, amplification of an incoming signal, was discussed in Chapter 2. In this chapter the two remaining functions, generation of a local oscillator signal and the heterodyning of the locally generated signal with the incoming signal to produce a third, or video-IF, signal, will be explained.

INCREMENTAL INDUCTANCE TUNER

The circuit in Figs. 3-1 and 3-2 shows the operation of the oscillator and mixer sections of a tuner which switches in additional sections of an incremental inductance for tuning. (The RF-amplifier section of this tuner was given in Figs. 2-1 and 2-2).

Identification of Components

The components which make up the circuit in Figs. 3-1 and 3-2 (and their principal functions) are as follows:

L19—Fixed inductor in series with RF-amplifier plate incremental inductances.

L20 through L25, L27 through L30—RF-amplifier plate incremental inductances.

L26, L43—Fixed inductors used in coupling the lower TV channels (2 through 6).

L31—Small inductance used for coupling high-band channels (7 through 13).

L32—Fixed inductor in series with mixer-grid incremental inductances.

L33 through L42—Mixer-grid circuit incremental inductances.

L44—Inductor portion of series LC combination between mixer screen grid and ground.

L45—Center-tapped inductor used as mixer plate load.

L46 through L57—Oscillator-grid circuit incremental inductances.

L58—Fixed inductor in series with oscillator incremental inductances.

C13—Capacitor portion of high-band coupling "gimmick."

C14—Capacitor portion of resonant peaking circuit used with the six low-frequency channels.

C15—Low-band coupling and blocking capacitor between RF-amplifier plate circuit and mixer grid circuit.

C16 and C17—Capacitors which resonate with mixer grid incremental inductances.

C18—Coupling and blocking capacitor between oscillator tank and mixer grid.

C19—Capacitor which resonates with L45 at the desired IF, but bypasses all higher frequencies to ground.

C20—Coupling and blocking capacitor to grid of first video-IF amplifier.

C21—Capacitor portion of series LC combination between mixer screen grid and ground.

C22—Coupling, blocking, and grid-leak storage capacitor for oscillator tube.

C23—Additional grid-leak storage capacitor for oscillator tube.

C24 and C25—Power-supply decoupling capacitors.

C26—Fine-tuning capacitor which resonates with oscillator incremental inductances (front-panel "operator" adjustment).

R6—Grid return resistor for V2A.

R7, R8—Screen-grid dropping resistors for V2A.

R9—Power-supply decoupling resistor.

R10—Grid-driving and grid-leakage resistor for V2A.

R11—Voltage-dropping resistor between power supply and oscillator plate.

R12—Resistor used to broaden the bandwidth response of coils L39 through L43 (used only for lower 5 channels).

Identification of Currents

There is a large number of different electron currents flowing in the various components of this circuit. Each electron current, however, is performing one or more necessary functions. Therefore, in order to fully understand the operation of the circuit, each of these currents at work must be visualized. They are:

1. RF-amplifier plate current (solid red).
2. Grid-driving current (at radio frequency) for mixer tube V2A (dotted blue).
3. Grid-driving current (at oscillator frequency) for V2A and V2B (solid green).
4. Mixer tube plate and screen grid current (also in solid red).
5. Oscillator tube plate current (also in solid red).
6. Grid-leakage current from V2A (dotted red).
7. Oscillating tank current (also in solid green).

Oscillator Circuit Actions

The ultra-audion oscillator circuit constructed around triode V2A is fairly typical of those used in modern TV receivers. The tuned tank circuit includes C26 in parallel with the incremental inductances (L46 through L57), as well as inductor L58. The plate current (solid red) flows only intermittently through V3. Its complete path takes it from ground through the tube, through some portion of the incremental inductances until contact is made with the shorting bar of the rotary switch, and then through L58, R11, and R9 to the power supply. As each pulse of this plate current reaches the tuned circuit, it excites and sustains an oscillation in the circuit.

The oscillating current (solid green) flows back and forth at the oscillator frequency between the upper plate of C26, through the inductances, to C22. C22, in turn, couples the action to the grid circuit of the tube. Fig. 3-1 shows a half-cycle of this tank current as it flows away from C26 and through the inductances toward the control grid. This flow direction drives the grid-driving current (solid green) downward through grid resistor R10, making the control grid negative and cutting off plate current through the tube.

On the next succeeding half-cycle of oscillation (Fig. 3-2), the tank current will flow in the opposite direction and draw the grid-driving current upward through R10, making the grid positive. This releases another pulsation of plate current through the tube and thus replenishes another cycle of oscillation. When the grid reaches its most positive value of voltage, it "captures" some of the electrons from the plate-current stream. These become the grid-leakage electrons shown in dotted red. They come out of the tube and accumulate on the right-hand plate of C22 and the upper plate of C23. Then they leak downward through R10 to ground and the cathode. This accumulation of electrons on the capacitors

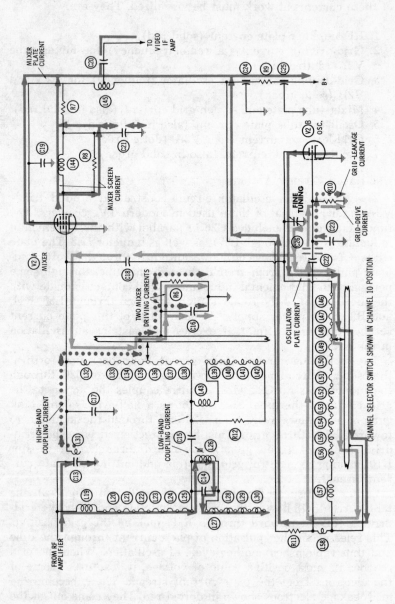

Fig. 3-1. Oscillator and mixer circuits used in a typical incremental-inductance tuner—shown tuned to Channel 10.

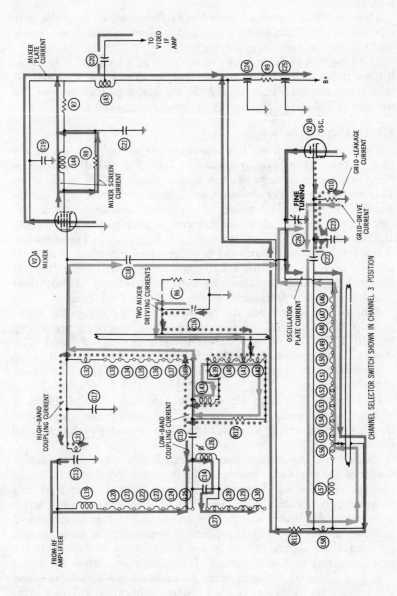

Fig. 3-2. Oscillator and mixer circuits used in a typical incremental-inductance tuner—shown tuned to Channel 3.

45

represents a permanent negative voltage, which is the grid-leak bias voltage.

This grid-leak current (dotted red) flows out of the tube only intermittently (once each cycle), but it flows continuously downward from the capacitors through R10.

The tank circuit is designed to oscillate at a frequency 45.75 mc higher than the incoming picture carrier. Thus, for Channel 10, which has channel limits of 192-198 mc and a picture carrier frequency of 163.25 mc, the oscillator frequency is 239 mc.

Mixer Circuit Action

The oscillations from the oscillator stage are coupled to the grid of the mixer tube by means of C18. Fig. 2-1 depicts a moment when the voltage on the upper plate of C26 is negative. This negative voltage drives some electron current upward toward C18; an equal number of electrons are driven from the upper plate of C18, downward through part of the inductances (L32 through L35), and through R6 to ground. The negative voltage which this downward movement of electrons creates at the top of R6 constitutes a half-cycle of grid-driving voltage at the grid of the mixer tube. The voltage developed at the mixer grid has the same frequency as the oscillator tank current.

A half-cycle later when the oscillator tank voltage on the upper plate of C26 reverses and becomes positive, electrons are drawn toward C26. This current flows upward through R6 and C16, through the incremental coils and L32, and downward through C18 toward C26. This constitutes a half-cycle of positive voltage at the mixer grid.

Resistor R12 is placed across the entire lower half of the bank of incremental inductances, thereby decreasing the response of the mixer grid circuit at each of the five lowest TV channels, (2 through 6).

There is no comparable requirement for broadening the bandwidth of the oscillator tank circuit. It is desired that this circuit operate at only one frequency for each channel and that this frequency be exactly 45.75 mc higher than the picture-carrier frequency. As shown in the composite waveform diagrams of Chapter 1, the title of picture-carrier frequency is given to one particular frequency, which is always 1.25 mc higher than the low-frequency end of the channel. For instance, when the set is tuned to Channel 3, the channel extends from 62 to 68 mc, and the picture frequency is 63.25 mc. The oscillator frequency must then be 109 mc.

Since the response of the oscillator tank does not need to be broadened, incremental inductances can be used to extend the tank frequency across the twelve TV channels (52 to 216 mc). There is no need to add extra capacitors or resistors in parallel with the incremental inductances (as was done in the other tuning circuits) to broaden the response.

At the same time that the oscillator signal is being coupled to the mixer grid, a signal from the RF-amplifier plate circuit is also being coupled to the mixer grid circuit. As the pulsations of plate current (solid red) flow through L19 through L30 in Fig. 3-1, some of the electrons are diverted onto the upper plate of C13. An equal number of electrons are then repelled from the lower plate of this capacitor and flow to ground. When tuned to one of the higher channels (as in Fig. 3-1), a device known as "gimmick coupling" is employed to transfer this signal to the mixer grid circuit. Although shown as a coil in Fig. 3-1, L31 actually consists of one or two turns of wire wound around the lead of C13. As an electron current pulsates through this lead, a similar electron flow is set up in L31. The high-band coupling current (dotted blue) flows from this point downward through L32 and a portion of the incremental inductances (L33, L34, and L35 in Fig. 3-1) until it reaches the shorting bar of the rotary switch. From the shorting bar, the current flows through R6 and C16 in parallel to ground.

On the next succeeding half-cycle of radio-frequency voltage, this current, which is in reality one of the grid-driving voltages for the mixer stage, reverses its direction and flows upward through C16 and the inductors. These inductors and C16 form another tuned-tank circuit which resonates at the frequency of the channel being received.

R6 is a high-value resistor (220,000 ohms) which diverts a relatively small amount of this resonant current away from C16. R6 is in the circuit to provide a "return path" from grid to cathode for any grid-leakage electrons which may be captured from the plate-current stream. Without such a grid return path, leakage electrons would eventually accumulate on the upper plate of C16, constituting a fixed negative voltage which would bias the mixer grid more and more negatively until that tube would be entirely cut off. This phenomenon is known as "grid blocking."

From the foregoing discussion it is evident that two separate high-frequency currents are flowing in the mixer grid circuit, and each one is developing an alternating voltage which "drives" the mixer grid. The signal current (dotted blue) develops one driving voltage, and the oscillator current (sometimes known as injection current) develops the other. Each of these driving voltages acts as a sort of "throttle" on the electron stream through the tube, and each voltage causes fluctuations (at its own frequency) in the amount of the plate current. In this manner, the two applied voltages are "mixed" in the mixer tube.

The electron stream through the tube is thus caused to vary in quantity at each of these two applied frequencies. But it will also vary at a number of additional frequencies, such as the sum of the two applied frequencies and the difference of the two frequencies. It is the so-called *difference* frequency which interests us at this time. There are some familiar mechanical analogies that might be useful in understanding or visualizing how a difference frequency is generated in this mixing process. The stroboscopic effect between wheels rotating at slightly different velocities is one such analogy. If the spokes of one wheel are observed through the spokes of the second wheel, an illusion will be created that wheel spokes are actually seen to be rotating at a very low velocity. This apparent velocity can be varied by changing the velocity of one of the wheels. The apparent rotational velocity of this illusion will prove to be the difference between the two wheel velocities—in other words, the difference frequency.

Another analogy familiar to those who may have flown in multi-engined propeller aircraft is the problem arising from unsynchronized engines. If two such engines are operated at slightly different engine speeds (rpm), a very unpleasant "beat" note is generated. These notes are at low frequencies and can be quite loud.

Both of the original current frequencies (carrier signal and oscillator) will be filtered to ground by capacitor C19. Likewise, all higher frequencies generated in the mixing process will be filtered to ground. However, the lowest one of these additional frequencies will not be filtered; instead, it will find an output circuit which offers it lower impedance or opposition than the filter circuit. Thus, the pulsations at the difference frequency will flow through the center-tapped inductor (L45) and will develop a voltage which becomes the output voltage at that frequency. This difference-frequency voltage will be coupled across C20 to the first video IF amplifier stage (not shown).

All of the plate current must flow downward through L45, but the pulsations which occur in this current at all higher frequencies find a path of lower impedance to ground by flowing first onto the upper plate of C19. The reason currents of different frequencies separate at the junction of the filter capacitor and the output inductor can be found in the formulas for capacitive reactance and inductive reactance:

$$X_C = \frac{1}{2\pi fC}$$

and,

$$X_L = 2\pi fL$$

Thus, from these formulas it is apparent that as frequencies become higher and higher, the capacitive reactance (X_c) becomes lower and lower. However, as the frequencies become lower, the inductive reactance (X_L) becomes lower.

The screen grid current (solid red) flows simultaneously through R8 and inductor L44. From here, they flow through the screen-dropping resistor (R7) and L45 toward the power supply. Since the plate-current stream through the tube is pulsating at many different frequencies the screen-grid current will exit from the tube as pulsating DC, with pulsations occurring at all of these frequencies. L44 and R8 act as an initial filter system to prevent these pulsations from reaching the plate circuit. However, these pulsations still have considerable strength when they reach the junction of R7 and C21. These latter two components operate as a conventional RC filter. Each pulsation of electrons flows initially onto the upper plate of C21, driving an equal number of electrons away from the lower plate and into ground. At the same time, there will be a continuous drain of electrons *away* from the upper plate of C21 and into R7. This electron flow through R7 generates a voltage drop across the resistor which must be subtracted from the value of voltage at the plate to determine the screen voltage. In this particular circuit, the plate voltage is 155 volts and the screen voltage is 140 volts.

The operation of the RL filter (R8 and L44) is interesting. Each pulsation of screen current attempts to enter the inductor, but the nature of any inductor is such that each entering pulsation generates a small "countercurrent" that flows through the inductor in a direction *opposite* to the pulsation (i.e., from right to left) and thus neutralizes or cancels the effect of the pulsation. This countercurrent flows only while the pulsation of current is *increasing*. When each pulsation ceases to increase (reaches its peak, in other words), the countercurrent which is generated dies out. As the pulsation dies out, another countercurrent which now flows *in the same direction* (from left to right) through L44 is generated. When each pulsation dies out completely, its new countercurrent also dies out.

It is by this seemingly frantic activity of countercurrents flowing in opposition to any changes (pulsations) in the screen grid current that the filter inductor (L44) tends to keep the changes in screen current from being passed further along the line toward the power supply.

The wires leading into C21 are also a scene of great activity; as each pulsation in the electron current exiting from the screen grid drives electrons onto the upper plate of the capacitor, an equal number flows away from the lower plate toward ground.

As each pulsation of screen current dies out, this flow direction reverses, with electrons being drawn away from the upper plate into R7, while other electrons are drawn up from ground onto the lower plate.

In these separate manners, both the filter inductor and capacitor act as "shock absorbers" to prevent unwanted fluctuations in the screen grid current from getting into the output circuit (L45 and C20).

TURRET TUNER

The oscillator and mixer circuit in Fig. 3-3 is employed in a tuner constructed using the turret principle. (The RF amplifier portion of this tuner was shown in Fig. 2-3.) Here, separate coils are employed for each channel. As the channel selector is switched to a given channel, the necessary coils to tune the circuits to the proper frequency are connected in the circuit.

Identification of Components

This circuit is composed of the following components which perform the indicated functions:

L9—Inductance component of amplifier plate circuit.

L10—Inductance component of mixer grid circuit.

L11—Inductance component of oscillator tank circuit.

L12—Variable inductance component of oscillator tank circuit (fine-tuning control).

L13—Fixed inductor in mixer plate circuit.

L14—Fixed inductor in mixer screen-grid circuit.

C13—Part of resonant tank leading to mixer grid.

C14—Coupling and blocking capacitor leading to mixer grid.

C15—Output coupling capacitor to video-IF amplifiers.

C16—Additional RF bypass capacitor in lead to video-IF amplifiers.

C17—Part of oscillator-circuit resonant tank.

C18—Coupling and blocking capacitor between oscillator tank and grid.

C19—Oscillator and mixer plate decoupling capacitor.

R5—Grid-driving resistor for mixer tube.

R6—Plate-load resistor for mixer tube.

R7—Grid resistor for oscillator tube.

R8—Plate-load resistor for oscillator tube.

R9—Plate decoupling resistor for oscillator and mixer tubes.

V2A—Pentode section of 5FG7 tube used as mixer.

V2B—Triode section of 5FG7 tube used as local oscillator.

Identification of Currents

Electron currents at work in this tuner and the colors in which they are shown are as follows:

1. RF-amplifier plate current (solid red).
2. Oscillator plate current (also in solid red).
3. Oscillator grid-leakage current (dotted red).
4. Oscillator tank current and grid-driving current (solid green).
5. Mixer tube plate current (also in solid red).
6. Mixer tube screen-grid current (also in solid red).
7. Signal-frequency grid-driving current for mixer tube (solid blue).
8. Oscillator-frequency grid-driving current for mixer tube (dotted green).

Oscillator Operation

A conventional triode oscillator (the triode portion of the 5FG7 tube) is used in Fig. 3-3. The operation of this circuit (V2B) is characterized by many features typical of oscillator operations, such as:

1. Plate current flows intermittently rather than continuously. This plate current (solid red) flows for much less than half of each cycle. This characteristic identifies it as Class-C operation.
2. A means of feeding energy back from the output (plate circuit) to the input (grid circuit). This means is provided in Fig. 3-3 by connecting the tuned circuit between the plate and grid of the tube.
3. A flow of grid-leakage current from the tube (dotted red) and the entrapment and accumulation of a substantial quantity of these electrons in the grid circuit to provide a grid-leak bias voltage.
4. A resonant-tank circuit in which a large "circulating" current can be built up. This current (solid green) is sustained in oscillation by feedback impulses which occur during every cycle of the oscillation. The oscillating current also "drives" the grid of the oscillator tube.
5. A means of utilizing the oscillation—in other words, coupling the oscillation to an output circuit.

As each burst of plate current flows through V2B, electrons will flow momentarily into the top of the tank circuit composed of L11, L12, and C17. This flow of electrons constitutes a feed-back action and helps sustain the oscillation. The oscillating tank current (solid green) in the instantaneous action (Fig. 3-3) is drawing current upward through grid resistor R7, making the grid momentarily positive. This positive grid releases a burst of plate-current flow through the tube. The positive grid attracts some electrons from the plate-current stream; these electrons (dotted red) become the grid-leak current. The grid-leak electrons exit from the tube at the grid and accumulate on the right-hand plate of C18, thus creating the negative grid-leak bias voltage. Eventually these grid-leak electrons flow downward through grid resistor R7 and return to the cathode of the tube.

Mixer Operation

Inductive coupling between L11 and L10 provides the means for transferring a portion of the oscillating energy to the mixer, or output, circuit. The continuous alternations in tank current flowing up and down in L11 will induce a companion current in L10. This latter current (dotted green) becomes one of the two driving currents at the grid of the mixer tube. The RF signal is both inductively and directly coupled via L10 to the mixer grid circuit. C13, which is connected in parallel with L12 to form a resonant-tank circuit, also functions as an adjustment to correct for slight deviations in the total circuit capacitance or induct-ance. This capacitor can be used to adjust the tuning for any of the twelve inductances switched into the position occupied by L10 when the various TV channels are selected. This tuned circuit (L10 and C13) makes it possible to build up a fairly strong oscil-latory current at the RF amplifier signal frequency in the mixer grid circuit. This grid-driving current (solid blue) is being drawn upward through the grid resistor (R5) and into the tuned grid circuit (L10 and C13) in Fig. 3-3. The upward movement of the current through R5 creates a positive voltage at the grid of V2A. During the next succeeding half-cycle, the current will move downward through R5, placing a negative voltage at the grid.

These voltage alternations at the grid of V2A will occur at the frequency of the incoming TV signal and will consequently cause the plate current of the mixer tube to vary or pulsate at this frequency.

As mentioned previously, a second grid-driving current (dotted green) is induced in L10 from L11. This current is forced up and down through R5 at the oscillator frequency. (You will recall that this frequency is exactly 45.75 mc higher than the incoming pic-ture carrier.) Thus, an alternating voltage at this oscillator fre-quency is developed at the mixer grid, causing its own independent set of variations or pulsations in the plate current through the mixer tube.

These two alternating voltages at the grid will cause many additional sequences of pulsations in the plate current through the mixer. We are interested only in capturing or utilizing that band of frequencies which represents the difference between the oscillator and the incoming signal frequencies. This band, which may cover 6 mc (from 41 to 47 mc), will be applied to a tuned circuit resonated to this band of frequencies in the video-IF input circuit. The amplification process of this difference frequency, which now becomes known as the IF (intermediate frequency), begins with the first video-IF amplifier. All of the other frequencies generated in the mixing process, plus the two applied frequencies, will be bypassed to ground in the video-IF amplifier input circuit. The first example of such a filter capacitor is found in C16—other filter arrangements follow this capacitor.

It can be seen that the plate currents from the oscillator tube and the mixer tube eventually flow together through R9 toward

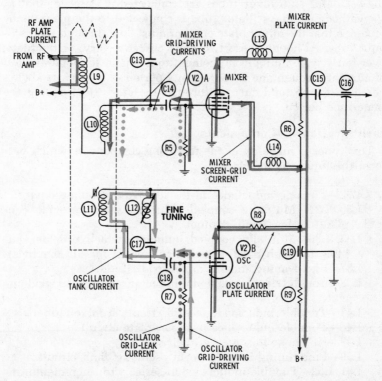

Fig. 3-3. Oscillator and mixer circuits used in a typical turret tuner.

the power supply. Capacitor C19 acts as a decoupling capacitor for the oscillator and mixer .plate currents. Any fluctuations in these currents which may still exist after passing through R8 and R6 respectively will drive current in and out of ground, utilizing the inherent capacitance between the inner and the outer conductors of the capacitor. In this type of capacitor, called a "feed-thru" capacitor, the inner lead is continuous and forms one plate of the capacitor. The outer covering which forms the other plate of the capacitor is then soldered directly to the chassis. If these undesirable current fluctuations can flow harmlessly to ground, they will be prevented ;from flowing through R9 to the power source. If they reach the power source, they cause its output voltage to fluctuate and thereby adversely affect any other tube circuit which is served by that output voltage.

CASCODE OSCILLATOR-MIXER CIRCUIT

The most significant difference in the circuit of Fig. 3-4 is that the oscillator and mixer tubes are connected in cascode; that is, the cathode of the oscillator tube is connected to the plate of the mixer so that the mixer plate current must flow through the oscillator tube. Although these two plate currents vary, or fluctuate, over fairly wide limits from moment to moment, the *total amount* of current through one tube over any period of time must always be equal to the total current through the other tube during the same time period.

Identification of Components

This tuner is made up of the following components which perform the functions indicated:

L32—Tunable inductance in the low-band coupling device.

L33, L34—Mutually coupled inductors which provide coupling for low-band channels.

L35, L36—Mutually coupled inductors which provide coupling for high-band channels (activated for all channels).

L37—Fixed inductance in mixer-grid circuit.

L38 through L46—Incremental inductances in mixer-grid circuit.

L47—Tunable inductance in grid circuit of mixer tube.

L48—Tunable inductance in mixer-plate circuit.

L49—RF choke in screen-grid circuit.

L50—Fine-tuning inductance in oscillator tank circuit.

L51, L52—Tunable inductance in series with incremental inductances.

L53 through L62—Incremental inductances in oscillator tank circuit.

R3—Grid-return resistor in mixer circuit.

R4—Resistor used for broadening response of incremental inductances.

R5—Plate-load resistor for mixer tube.

R6—Isolating resistor between mixer plate and oscillator cathode.

R7—Grid-driving and grid-return resistor for oscillator tube.

R8—Plate-load resistor for oscillator tube.

C10—Coupling and blocking capacitor between oscillator tank and mixer grid.

C11—Capacitor for broadening response of mixer-grid tank circuit.

C12—Capacitor for resonating with inductor L48.

C13—Mixer plate circuit decoupling capacitor.

C14—Grid-leak storage capacitor for oscillator.

C15—Capacitor for broadening response of incremental inductances.

C16—Feedback capacitor between plate and tank circuit of oscillator.

C17—Oscillator plate circuit decoupling capacitor.

V2A—Pentode portion of 6EA8 tube used as a mixer.

V2B—Triode portion of 6EA8 tube used as oscillator.

Identification of Currents

The electron currents flowing in this circuit and the colors in which they are shown are as follows:

1. RF-amplifier plate current (solid red).
2. Mixer grid-driving current at signal frequency (dotted blue).
3. Mixer grid-driving current at oscillator frequency (solid green).
4. Mixer and oscillator plate current (solid red).
5. Oscillator tank current (solid green).
6. Oscillator grid-leakage current (dotted red).

Details of Operation

Two currents are being coupled to the mixer stage in Fig. 3-4. The first is the signal from the RF-amplifier stage. (The RF-amplifier stage of this tuner was given in Fig. 2-4.) L35 and L36 provide inductive coupling between the RF-amplifier plate circuit and the mixer grid incremental inductance for the high-band channels. This induced current (dotted blue) flows up and down through incremental inductances connected in the circuit, as well as L47. When the shorting bar passes L34 in going from Channel 7 to Channel 6, the low-band coupling inductors (L33 and L34) are inserted in their respective circuits. The lower coupling coils (L35 and L36), which provide high-band coupling, remain activated when the lower channels are being received.

The mixer plate current (solid red) flows in a continuous stream (Class-A operation). This current stream is caused to vary in quantity by the two driving currents in the grid circuit so that both of these driving frequencies are reproduced. The difference between these two frequencies will also be produced, and the current pulsations which occur at this new frequency of 45.75 mc will be coupled into the video IF amplifier strip.

Screen-grid current (solid red) also flows out of V2A. Like most screen currents, this one serves no useful purpose; it is the inevitable result of placing a high positive voltage on the screen grid in order to increase the electron flow through the tube. Inductor L49 acts like a radio-frequency choking device so that the various pulsations in this screen current are partially damped out or eliminated before they reach R6. This resistor along with capacitor C13 furnishes additional decoupling so that all remaining current fluctuations in either the plate current or the screen current will be bypassed harmlessly to ground by C13. Thus, when these tube currents enter R6, they are flowing as pure DC. This is important because they must now flow through oscillator tube V2A; it is desirable that the only fluctuations in the oscillator tube current be those which are imposed by the oscillator tank current.

Plate current flows through the oscillator tube in short bursts. This current flows whenever the control grid is momentarily raised above the cutoff voltage value. At the instant of time depicted in Fig. 3-4, a burst of plate current is flowing. This current drives a feedback impulse into the right-hand plate of C16, which supports and replenishes the oscillation in the tank circuit (made up of L50 through L62, C14, and C15). Also, when plate current flows, some grid-leakage electrons flow out of the tube and accumulate on the upper plate of C14, building up a negative grid-leak bias voltage (dotted red). These electrons eventually get back to the cathode by flowing downward through R7. It is the large size of R7 that effectively traps these electrons on C14 and causes them to accumulate into a substantial negative voltage (indicated by the red minus signs).

The oscillator tank current is shown in solid green. The resulting tank voltage drives an electron current upward onto the lower plate of C10. A corresponding number of electrons flow upward from the upper plate of C10 to the grid circuit of the mixer tube.

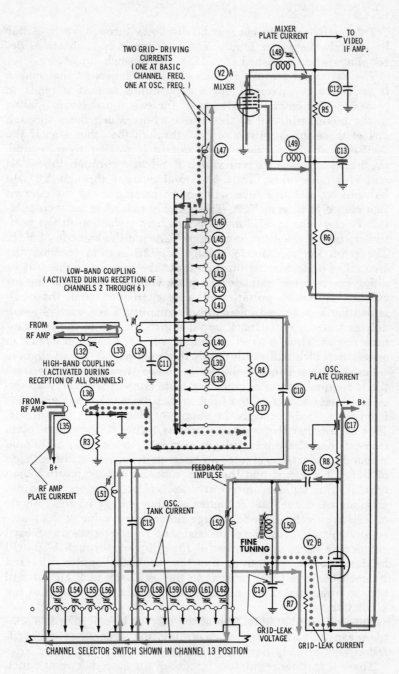

Fig. 3-4. A typical cascode oscillator and mixer circuit.

The oscillator plate current finally flows through load resistor R8 and into the power supply. The filtering process, known as decoupling, is accomplished by C17, a feedthrough capacitor.

The particular feature of the cascode arrangement that makes it attractive in mixer-oscillator applications is that it tends to provide an automatic regulation of the two signal levels applied to the mixer grid. All of the tube current which flows through one of these tubes must also flow through the other one. If the oscillation in the oscillator tank circuit is weaker than desired, the bursts of plate current which it releases through tube V2B will also be weaker. Thus, the total current through V2 will be reduced, and this tube will not be passing all of the current that comes to it from V2A. This quickly results in an accumulation of electrons on C13 and a consequent reduction in the positive voltage applied to the plate of V2A and the cathode of V2B. The reduction in cathode voltage of V2B acts to *increase* the amount of plate current through that tube because of the greater difference between cathode and plate voltages applied to the oscillator tube. Each pulsation of plate current through the oscillator tube is increased in amount or quantity. Thus, each one will deliver a stronger feedback impulse through C16 to the resonant tank circuit. Thus, a weak oscillation will set a chain of events in operation which will result finally in strengthening the oscillation.

On the other hand, if the oscillation is stronger than desired, the individual bursts of oscillator plate current will carry an excess of electrons across the tube so that the demand for electrons from the cathode exceeds the supply of electrons to the cathode. This means that the oscillator tube is trying to pass more plate current than the mixer tube is supplying to it. This additional demand for electrons creates an electron deficiency at the cathode of V2B. This means that the voltage becomes more positive than normal. This build-up in positive voltage actually occurs on decoupling capacitor C13. A higher positive voltage on the cathode of V2B brings the cathode voltage closer to the value of the plate-supply voltage; thus, the plate current flow is decreased and each succeeding burst or pulsation of tube current through V2B will be decreased in strength so that the feedback impulse delivered by each burst of plate current to the oscillator tank circuit will also be weakened. This results in diminishing the strength of the oscillation.

This self-regulating feature of the cascode circuit affords a simple means of controlling, or governing, the strength of the oscillation within fairly narrow limits.

There is another regulating feature of the cascode circuit which is important. Variations may also occur in the signal strength of the incoming carrier signal. These variations may occur in a single channel due to atmospheric or propagation anomalies, or they may occur when you are switching from one channel to another, due to substantial differences in radiated power or to variations in distance between transmitter and receiver. Any such variations in signal strength are partially, but not entirely, compensated for by the automatic gain control (AGC) feature in all receivers. It is desirable that a strong incoming signal be matched with a strong oscillator signal and that a weak incoming RF signal be matched with a weak oscillator signal. The conduction characteristics of the typical pentode tube, even a sharp cutoff pentode, ensure that this important condition will be met. A study of the characteristic curves in Fig. 3-5 reveals why this is possible.

Two examples of a single cycle of radio-frequency signal voltage superimposed on a typical characteristic curve for a sharp cutoff pentode are given in Fig. 3-5. In Fig. 3-5A the peak-to-peak value of the signal voltage is 2 volts and the tube has an operating bias of −2 volts. Thus, the signal voltage causes the grid voltage to vary between the extremes of −1 and −3 volts. This signal voltage at the grid causes the plate current to vary between the extremes of 17 and 36 milliamperes. These values are chosen to coincide with the plate-voltage line of +100 volts, which is a typical value for this application. The *average* amount of plate current which this size signal causes to flow in the mixer pentode is approximately 26 milliamperes.

Fig. 3-5B shows the significant change in plate current that occurs when the incoming signal becomes twice as strong so that it now causes the grid voltage to vary between zero and −4 volts. The plate current now varies between values of 8 and 51 milliamperes, with an *average* plate current of approximately 29 mils.

These two examples show that the pentode tube passes more total plate current when receiving strong signals than when receiving weak signals. This tends to force more electrons to the cathode of the oscillator tube, and if the oscillator is operating at a low level, it will not be prepared to accept this additional current. Thus, electrons quickly accumulate at the cathode of V2B and reduce its positive voltage. This has the effect (described previously) of increasing the amount of plate current, because of the greater differential in voltages at the cathode and plate of the oscillator. Each burst of oscillator tube current is increased in amount, the feedback impulses are strengthened, and the oscillator tank current is strengthened. Thus, we can see that the cascode arrangement as used here will automatically encourage the generation of a strong oscillator signal when the incoming TV signal is strong.

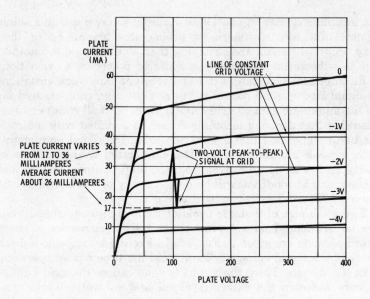

(A) Small grid signal.

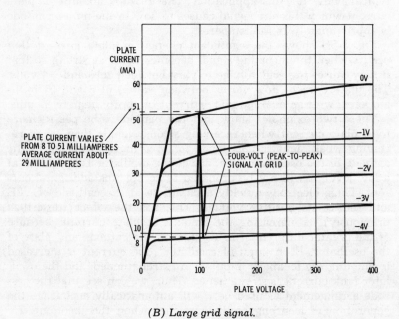

(B) Large grid signal.

Fig. 3-5. Characteristic curves for a sharp-cutoff pentode tube.

Working backward from Fig. 3-5B to 3-5A, we can demonstrate that as an incoming signal weakens in strength, it will cause a smaller total amount of plate current to pass through the amplifier tube. This results in a scarcity of electron current available as plate current for the oscillator tube. This scarcity, or deficiency, of electrons quickly translates into a rise in positive voltage at the oscillator cathode. This voltage rise reduces the difference in voltage between oscillator plate and cathode so that each burst of plate current will be reduced in size, the feedback impulses will be reduced in strength, and the oscillation weakened accordingly.

Typical operating voltages for this cascode arrangement might use a B+ supply voltage of about +250 volts applied to the oscillator plate. The oscillator cathode would settle down at about half this value, or +125 volts. The steady flow of plate current downward through resistor R6 (a 2,200-ohm resistor) will cause an additional voltage drop of perhaps 20 or 25 volts so that a remainder of 100 volts is available as plate voltage for the amplifier tube. Obviously these values will vary as the average amount of pentode plate current is varied in the manner explained in the previous examples.

REVIEW QUESTIONS

1. By what action or actions is a voltage at the oscillator frequency developed at the grid of mixer tube V2 in the incremental inductance tuner?

2. You have learned that every electron current must be "driven" by another independent action, such as another current or voltage. In Figs. 3-1 and 3-2, what "drives" the two currents labelled as low-band and high-band coupling currents?

3. Why is capacitor C19 (Figs. 3-1 and 3-2) able to bypass all frequencies except the desired IF (intermediate frequency) to ground?

4. The turret tuner section of this chapter lists five features which are frequently characteristic of oscillator operation. Which, if any, of these features are *not* present in the ultra-audion oscillator of Fig. 3-1?

5. By what circuit action is a voltage at the local oscillator frequency developed at the grid of mixer tube V2 in the turret tuner (Fig. 3-3)?

6. Describe the path of plate currents through the cascode tubes V2A and V2B, in Fig. 3-4. Does the plate current through each of these tubes flow continuously or intermittently?

7. If the incoming signal strength decreases, will the "self-regulating" feature of the cascode circuit cause a decrease or an increase in the positive voltage at the cathode of V2B? Will this increase or decrease the strength of the individual cycles of oscillation?

8. If very weak signals are received, how does the cascode operate to reduce the strength of the oscillator voltage?

Chapter 4

VIDEO-IF AMPLIFIERS

The primary function of the video-IF amplifier strip in a TV receiver is to provide the necessary amplification to the signal delivered by the tuner. In addition to amplification, however, trap circuits must be included in any video-IF amplifier in order to obtain the desired response. In the following pages a two- and a three-tube video-IF amplifier will be analyzed in detail. Other circuits will employ essentially the same methods as the ones used as examples in this chapter to obtain the desired response.

TWO-TUBE VIDEO-IF AMPLIFIER CIRCUIT

The principal circuit actions that occur in a typical two-tube video-IF amplifier circuit are shown in Fig. 4-1. This circuit must amplify the IF signal delivered to it from the tuner, filter out any unwanted signals, and deliver the amplified signals to the following stages. Fig. 4-2 shows the desired response curve of a video-IF amplifier strip. It can be seen that the strip should provide equal amplification to frequencies within roughly a 4-mc band. At the upper end of this band the response should drop off gradually and uniformly so that the response (amplification) will be exactly 50% of maximum at the so-called video-IF carrier frequency of 45.75 mc.

Identification of Components

The video-IF strip in Fig. 4-1 is made up of the following circuit components which perform the functions indicated:

L1—Inductor portion of 47.25-mc parallel-resonant trap.
L2—Inductor used for series-peaking at 42.7 mc.
L3—Plate-load inductor for V1.

L4—Inductor used for transformer coupling to grid circuit of V2.

L5—Plate-load inductor for V2.

L6—Inductor used for transformer coupling to video detector.

C1—Capacitor used for blocking AGC voltage from ground (also part of trap circuit).

C2—Capacitor portion of a 47.25-mc parallel-resonant trap.

C3—AGC storage capacitor.

C4—Power-supply decoupling capacitor.

C5—Cathode filter capacitor for V2.

C6—Screen-grid filter capacitor for V2.

C7—Capacitor for resonating with L6 at 47.2 mc.

C8—Integrating capacitor for accumulating the output video voltage.

R1—Grid-driving and grid-return resistor for V1.

R2—Resistor which broadens the response of L2.

R3—Cathode resistor used to provide some degeneration.

R4—Resistor which broadens response of L3.

R5, R6—Voltage-divider resistors.

R7—Cathode-biasing resistor for V2.

R8—Power-supply decoupling resistor.

Note: In addition to the preceding, the dashed lines indicate distributed capacitance in parallel with L2, L3, L4, and L5.

Identification of Currents

The following electron currents, shown in the colors indicated, will flow in this circuit during signal reception:

1. Input-signal current (solid blue).
2. Resonant-trap current at 47.25 mc (dotted red).
3. Resonant-peaking current at 42.7 mc (dotted blue).
4. Plate current through both amplifier tubes (solid red).
5. Screen-grid current through both amplifier tubes (also in dotted red).
6. Resonant-peaking current at 44.3 mc (solid green).
7. Resonant-peaking current at 44.2 mc (dotted green).
8. Voltage-divider current (also in dotted red).
9. Detector-output (video) current (also in solid blue).
10. Power-supply decoupling currents (also in dotted blue).
11. AGC current (also in solid green).

Details of Operation

The input-signal current (solid blue) enters the IF strip from the output of the mixer tube (see Chapter 3). This current is

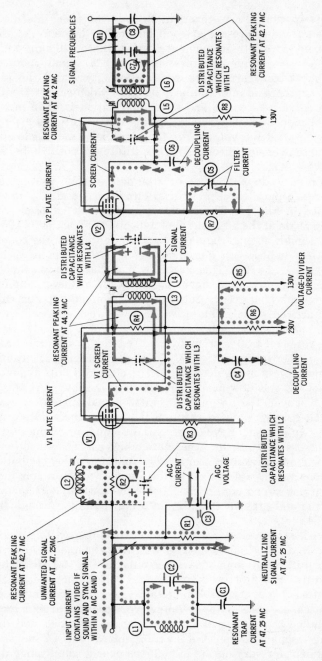

Fig. 4-1. Operation of a two-stage video-IF strip.

driven up and down through R1 at whatever intermediate-frequency value present at each particular moment. As will be explained more fully in the next chapter, there will almost always be two such frequencies present—the FM signal centered at 41.25 mc which carries the audio information, and the picture and synchronizing information. The basic video-carrier frequency which carries the video and sync information is 45.75 mc. Each current movement downward through R1 constitutes a negative half-cycle of drive voltage for the amplifier tube. Each upward current movement through R1 constitutes a positive half-cycle of drive voltage.

In order to de-emphasize, or attenuate, certain unwanted frequencies, a parallel-resonant trap circuit (L1 and C2) has been included in Fig. 4-1. These two components are chosen so they will resonate at the adjacent channel sound-IF carrier (47.25 mc). If any signals at this frequency have come through the tuner circuit, they will set up and maintain an oscillation of electrons through L1 and C2. The circuit will act as a trap, effectively "killing" the unwanted signal at this point in the circuit by the interaction which occurs between the resonant-trap current and the undesired signal. This interaction between the two currents works in the following manner.

The resonant trap current (dotted red in Fig. 4-1) delivers electrons to the upper plate of C2, thereby charging it negatively. This negative voltage normally drive electrons out of the upper plate of C2 and downward through R1, as shown. At the same time, however, the original unwanted signal current is drawing electron current upward through R1, as shown in dotted green. These two currents develop essentially equal and opposing voltages across this resistor; therefore, they cancel each other out. The original unwanted signal also reinforces the oscillation of electrons which is going on in the tuned circuit. In this manner the parallel tuned circuit can "trap" the particular frequency of 47.25 mc and prevent its entry into and passage through the IF amplifiers.

In order to develop an IF response curve that will approximate the desired shape shown in Fig. 4-2, the principle of series peaking is utilized at four separate points in Fig. 4-1. Inductor L2 constitutes the first of these points. This inductor is specially wound so that its natural inductance and the distributed or inherent capacitance of the winding will resonate at 42.7 mc. The distributed capacitance is indicated by dashed lines, and the resulting resonant current is shown by dotted blue. L2 has a screw adjustment for varying the inductance over a small range during the alignment process.

In the alignment procedure a signal from a signal generator operating at this frequency is applied to the input point at the left edge of the diagram, and an oscilloscope is connected across the output tank circuit (L6 and C7). Since only a single frequency is being applied to the input, the response curve viewed on the oscilloscope face will be a single-humped curve like that shown in Fig. 4-2 (labeled as the 42.7-mc resonant peak). Slight adjustments should now be made to variable inductors L2 and L6 until this individual response curve is brought to its maximum possible amplitude. When this maximum amplitude is achieved, the resonant currents (dotted blue) will be flowing back and forth within the confines of the tuned circuits at the maximum attainable strength.

Similar adjustments are made on inductors L3, L4, and L5 at the different frequencies indicated on the diagram of circuit actions. For instance, a signal-generator frequency of 44.3 mc is applied to the circuit input, and L3 and L4 are jointly adjusted until the appropriate single-humped curve of Fig. 4-2 reaches its maximum possible amplitude. This tells us that the resonant or circulating current (solid green) is flowing at maximum strength.

L5 is adjusted with the signal generator tuned to 44.2 mc. As before, adjust the appropriate response curve on the oscilloscope for maximum amplitude. The circulating current shown in dotted green will then be flowing at maximum strength.

Two of these peaking inductors (L2 and L3) have been paralleled with resistors. These resistors broaden, or widen, the response curves at the particular frequencies involved; however, they also cause a considerable reduction in the amplitude of the curve. The solid lines on Fig. 4-2 indicate the sharper response curves attainable at these two frequencies (42.7 and 44.3 mc) if R2 and R4 were removed from the circuit. Since the ideal response curve of the entire circuit is the composite sum of the individual response curves, the sharper curves indicated in the solid lines would require that other circuit adjustments be devised in order to achieve the desired flat response.

The voltage-divider current (dotted red) which flows upward through R5 and downward through R6 exists for the sole purpose of providing an intermediate value of positive voltage for the plate and screen grids of tube V1. The power supply for this receiver (not shown here) provides sources of 130 volts and 230 volts. The designer of this circuit needed approximately 160 volts at plate and screen for optimum operation; the values of R5 and R6 were chosen to provide such a voltage.

Both amplifier tubes (V1 and V2) operate under Class-A conditions, meaning that their plate currents flow continuously. These currents are pulsating direct currents whose fluctuations are regulated by the signal voltages applied to their respective control grids. Fluctuations or pulsations in these plate currents must occur at every frequency contained in the incoming signal frequency. These pulsations then induce true alternating currents (oscillations of electrons) in the tuned plate circuits (L3 and L5, respectively, along with their distributed capacitances). The final appearance of the video-IF signal then occurs across the tuned circuit at the detector input (L6 and C7). This signal current should contain all of the frequencies present in the input signal current, but in greatly amplified, or strengthened, form. While a resonant-peaking current has been shown (dotted blue) oscillating back and forth between C7 and L6 at the frequency of 42.7 mc, all other currents occurring in the entire passband (41 through 47 mc) will also cause oscillations along this path. On each negative half-cycle of any such oscillation, electrons will be driven from left to right through video detector M1. A negative half-cycle has been indicated in Fig. 4-1, with electrons massed on the upper plate of C7. The current which flows to the right through M1 builds up an accumulation of electrons (negative voltage) on the upper plate of C8. The negative voltage becomes known as the video voltage; its presence on C8 marks its first appearance as an identifiable voltage in the receiver. Until this point the information, or intelligence, which brings it about has been "carried" by the RF and IF signals in the form of modulation.

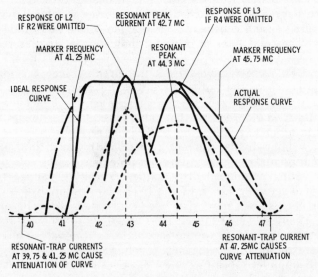

Fig. 4-2. Typical video-IF response.

Electrons cannot be added indefinitely to the top of C8 without some provision being made for their removal. This removal or leakage process occurs through the output circuit (not shown here). The detector output circuit becomes the input circuit for the video amplifier (discussed in Chapter 5).

C5 serves as a cathode-bypass capacitor for V2. A filter current (dotted red) flows up and down through this circuit at each and every frequency contained in the input signal. As each positive pulsation in the signal occurs, extra plate-current electrons must leave the cathode and flow through the tube. These additional electrons are more easily drawn from the upper plate of C5 than through R7, because the capacitive reactance (impedance) of C5 is much lower than the resistance of R7 at the high frequencies we are working with here. In the short period following each such pulsation of plate current, electrons which are flowing continuously upward through R7 will spill over onto the top plate of C5 and drive electron current downward from the lower plate of C5 toward ground. This movement of electrons constitutes the second half-cycle of each filter action.

No similar filter action can occur at the cathode of V1, since no filter or bypass capacitor is bridged across R3. In the absence of such a filter capacitor, degeneration or some loss in signal amplification will occur. As each pulsation of plate current flows into V1 from the cathode, it must be drawn in its entirety up from ground through R3. This causes a momentary rise in positive voltage at the cathode. This rise, in effect, *opposes* the positive rise in grid voltage that caused it. The amount of this degenerative action is determined by the size of R3. In this circuit, it is a 43-ohm resistor, so the loss in amplification will be slight. The principal advantage of such a planned degenerative action is that it prevents a tuned-grid, tuned-plate amplifier from breaking into oscillation. In addition, the total current "drain" from the power supply is lessened. The word "drain" is emphasized here because it implies something being drained *away* from the power supply. Actually, all plate-current electrons drain *into* the power supply, but their total quantity determines the magnitude of the requirement which is placed on a power supply to "deliver" current to the tubes.

Power-supply decoupling currents flow through capacitors C4 and C6. These are alternating currents similar in nature to the cathode-bypass current which flows up and down through C5. It is absolutely essential that all of the pulsations in the plate current through these tubes be removed, or filtered, to ground, *after* they have performed their tasks in the plate-load circuit but *before* they reach the power supply. If any of these pulsations reach the power supply, they will be re-applied, or fed back, to earlier amplifier circuits. This feedback will fulfill the conditions necessary for self-sustained oscillations of one or more amplifier stages. Thus, the amplifiers would then be unusable for their primary function of signal amplification. To obviate the possibility of unwanted oscillations due to signal feedback through the power suply, simple RC filters are interposed between the plate-load circuits and the power supply.

R6 and C4 constitute one such filter, and R8 and C6 constitute a second one. The actions occurring in each one are identical. In each plate-load circuit there is a condition of resonance between the plate-load inductors and the combined distributed and interelectrode capacitances. Whenever a negative voltage peak appears at the bottom of one of these tank circuits, it tends to drive electrons into the power supply. When an RC filter is placed between the two points, such a voltage pulsation is presented with two alternate choices—either to flow onto the upper plate of the capacitor (a negligible impedance at high frequencies) or to flow into the much higher resistance path offered by R6 or R8.

In Fig. 4-1 the decoupling current is flowing onto the upper plate of C4, driving an equal number of electrons away from the lower plate and into ground. This action constitutes a single half-cycle of decoupling action. It must inevitably be followed by a return flow of electrons upward from ground onto the lower plate of C4. Other electrons are drawn away from the upper plate and into the power supply along with the rest of the plate current. The decoupling sequence repeats itself millions of times each second; the result is that the plate and screen currents that enter R6 and the power supply are largely smoothed out, or filtered.

The second half-cycle of a similar decoupling sequence is indicated at C6. Here electrons are being drawn away from the upper plate of C6 and into the power supply, while an equal number of electrons are being drawn upward from ground onto the lower plate. This action will occur whenever a positive peak of voltage appears at the bottom of the plate-load circuit (L5 in a resonant condition with its own distributed capacitance plus the interelectrode capacitance of amplifier tube V2).

Automatic Gain Control

The control grid of V1 is connected directly to the upper plate of the AGC capacitor (C3). This is a very large capacitor; hence, a large accumulation of electrons appears on it during normal operation. This accumulation of electrons constitutes a negative voltage (indicated by the green minus signs), which is applied as a biasing voltage to the control grid of V1. This AGC voltage is "fed" by the AGC current (solid green) which flows alternately into and out of it. During any sustained period when the incoming signal maintains a constant strength or amplitude, the AGC voltage will not change in value. If the signal should fade (decrease), the amount of the AGC voltage also decreases, thereby increasing the amplification provided by V1. This change in AGC voltage is brought about by changing the amount of the AGC current so that the quantity of electrons which flows into C3 during a series of negative half-cycles will be less than the quantity which flows away from C3 during a series of positive half-cycles. The net effect is to drain electrons away from the storage pool on C3 and decrease the negative AGC voltage.

If the incoming signal should increase in strength, the negative AGC voltage should also increase to reduce the gain of V1. This is accomplished by increasing the quantity of electrons flowing into C3 during a negative half-cycle.

The AGC current flows back and forth at the sync-pulse frequency of 15,750 cycles per second. A negative half-cycle that delivers electrons into the storage pool on C3 is shown in Fig. 4-1. (The development of an AGC voltage for TV receivers has been treated in much greater detail in the companion text, *TV Sync and Deflection Circuit Actions.*)

Two general principles are used in video-IF amplifiers to achieve the necessary bandwidth. They are the principle of over-coupled transformers and the principle of staggered tuning. In the average circuit diagram it is not always easy to distinguish between the two principles. An overcoupled transformer can usually be identified by the arrangements made for double tuning. In other words, both primary and secondary windings may be tuned independently by the small tuning slugs indicated above each winding. In the overcoupled transformer principle the primary and secondary are usually tuned separately to the same frequency. The degree of coupling between the two windings is increased to the point where twin resonant peaks occur, one on either side of a center frequency. L5 and L6 fall in this category. When these two inductors are jointly tuned, resonant peaks should occur at 44.2 and 42.7 mc.

L3 and L4 have a single tuning slug for both windings. This usually indicates that the windings are not intended to be over-coupled; instead, they should be tuned to a single frequency. It also indicates that they are being used in a staggered-tuning principle. The resonant peaking current indicated in windings L3 and L4 flows at 44.3 mc. This frequency combines adequately with the other peaking currents to produce the desired IF response curve shown in Fig. 4-2.

THREE-TUBE VIDEO-IF AMPLIFIER CIRCUIT

Fig. 4-3 shows the circuit actions which occur in a somewhat more elaborate video-IF strip than the one previously described. This circuit uses three pentode amplifier stages. It also provides three resonant trap circuits for the attenuation or elimination of unwanted frequencies.

Identification of Components

The components included in this video-IF strip and their functions are as follows:

L1—Inductor portion of 47.25-mc trap.

L2—Inductor portion of 39.25-mc trap.

L3—Inductor portion of 41.25-mc trap.

L4, L5—Inductors in input tuned transformer.

L6, L7—Inductors in tuned transformer between V1 and V2.

L8, L9—Inductors in tuned transformer between tubes V2 and V3.

L10, L11—Inductors in output tuned transformer.

C1—Capacitor that blocks AGC voltage from leaking to ground through L1.

C2—Capacitor portion of 47.25-mc trap.

C3—Capacitor portion of 39.25-mc trap.

C4—Capacitor that blocks AGC voltage from leaking to ground through R3.

C5—Capacitor portion of 41.25-mc trap.

C6—Screen-grid filter capacitor for V1.

C7—Decoupling capacitor between plate of V1 and cathode of V2.

C8—V2 screen-grid filter and plate-decoupling capacitor.

C9—Cathode-filter capacitor for V3.

C10—V3 screen-grid filter and plate-decoupling capacitor.

C11—Capacitor which resonates with L11.

C12—Detector output capacitor.

C13—AGC storage capacitor.

C14—Distributed and interelectrode capacitance of V1 plate circuit.

C15—Distributed and interelectrode capacitance of V2 grid circuit.

C16—Distributed and interelectrode capacitance of V2 plate circuit.

C17—Distributed and interelectrode capacitance of V3 grid circuit.

R1—Resistor for broadening the response of L4.

R2—Decoupling resistor between input grid circuit and the AGC system.

R3—Grid-driving resistor for V1.

R4—Cathode-biasing resistor for V1.

R5—Screen-grid dropping resistor.

R6, R7—Voltage-dividing network which biases grid and cathode of V2.

R8—Resistor for broadening the response of L7.

R9, R10—Voltage-divider network.

R11—Cathode-biasing resistor for V2.

R12—Decoupling resistor between plate tank of V2 and 250-volt power supply.

R13—Resistor for broadening the response of L9.

R14—Cathode-biasing resistor for V3.

R15—Voltage-divider resistor (operates in conjunction with R14).

R16, R17—Voltage-divider network for setting the operating voltage at plate of V3.

Identification of Currents

The following electron currents, which are depicted in the colors indicated, flow in this video-IF amplifier strip during normal operation:

1. Input IF signal current (solid blue).
2. Resonant-trap currents at 47.25, 41.25, and 39.25 mc (solid green).
3. Plate and screen-grid currents through the three amplifier tubes (solid red).
4. Resonant-peaking currents at 45.5 and 43.0 mc (dotted green).
5. Three voltage-divider currents (dotted red).
6. Video-detector current (also in solid blue).
7. AGC current for maintaining a negative voltage on C13 (also in solid green).
8. Decoupling currents through C6, C8, and C10 (dotted blue).
9. Cathode-filter current through C9 (also in dotted blue).

Details of Operation

Most of the fundamental principles discussed earlier in this chapter are repeated in the circuit of Fig. 4-3. Therefore these principles will not be restated as they occur, unless they incorporate some new feature.

One important feature of this circuit is the use of the cascode connection, whereby the first two amplifier stages (V1 and V2) are placed in series with each other so that the same stream of electron current must flow through both tubes. The complete path of these currents is through R4, V1, L6, R6, R11, V2, L8, and R12 before entering the 250-volt power supply. An additional component of the plate current through V1 is shown as joining this current stream at the junction of R6 and R7 after flowing upward through R9 and down through R7. The amount of this special component of plate current is closely related to the cascode relationship between the two tubes.

The operation of these tubes can be explained in the following manner.

Resistors R9 and R10 are large-value resistors (150,000 ohms each) that provide operating voltages to the plate and screen grid of V1, as well as to the control grid and cathode of V2. The voltage divider current (dotted red) flows upward from ground through R9 and down through R10. The result of this current flow is the development of a voltage of 125 volts at the junction of the two resistors. In the absence of any other current flow, this voltage exists at the four tube electrodes mentioned previously. When this 125 volts is applied to the plate and screen of V1, the streams of plate current and screen-grid current electrons are drawn across the tube. In flowing downward through R6 these currents develop an additional voltage drop across R6 so that the final voltage applied to the plate and screen grid is approximately 105 volts.

V1 and V2 are similar type tubes. With identical operating voltages applied to the various electrodes, the two tubes should conduct identical quantities of current (normally about 14 milliamperes). If for any reason the current flow through V1 is reduced, the extra electrons required by V2 would be supplied from the current which flows upward through R9 and down through R7. In flowing down through R7, the current biases the control grid of V2 more negatively than before with respect to the cathode of V2. This reduces the total current flowing through the tube and tends to bring it more in line with the amount of current through V1. Thus the electron current through R7 acts as a sort of regulator.

If for any reason the total current through V1 should increase above normal values, it would tend to create a less positive voltage at the junction of R6 and R11. Even by itself this reduction in positive voltage at the lower end of R11 would amount to an increase in "positive" bias for V2 so that it will conduct additional electrons. Also the difference in voltage between the top and bottom of R7 will be of such polarity that some of the plate current from V1 may be diverted and drawn upward through R7 toward the more positive voltage at the junction of R9 and R10. This will make the upper terminal of R7 more positive than the lower terminal. Since the control grid of V2 is connected to this point, it constitutes an additional component of positive bias to increase the current flow through V2. Thus the electron current through R7 can vary in both direction and amount. By so doing, it acts as a "regulator" to keep the plate currents through V1 and V2 essentially equal to each other.

The most obvious causes of variations in the plate current of V1 are changes in the AGC voltage on C13. These changes are brought about by variations in the strength of the incoming signal. The AGC voltage makes possible a reduction in the total amplification provided for a strong signal and increases the amplification of a weak signal. A strong signal generates a large negative AGC voltage and tends to reduce the total electron current through V1. The resultant decrease in current through V2 also causes this tube to operate under a condition of reduced amplification. Hence, AGC voltage applied to V1 affects both tubes.

An opposite sequence of events will occur with a weak signal. The negative AGC voltage on C13 will be decreased, moving the operating point of V1 in a direction that provides increased amplification of each individual cycle of the signal, as well as an increase in the total amount of plate current. This increase in plate current through V1 moves the operating point for V2 in a direction that also causes V2 to provide greater amplification of the applied video signal.

When the circuit is ideally designed, the two amplifiers should provide equal amplification or gain. Thus, a cascode arrangement is in the nature of a matching device to assure that equal amplification is attained.

Two voltage-divider currents are used to regulate the operation of V3. The first of these (dotted red) flows upward through R14 and downward through R15 toward the power supply, thus placing a small positive voltage at the cathode of V3. The plate current for this tube (solid red), in flowing upward through R14, will also contribute a very small portion of the positive cathode voltage—only a small fraction of a volt. The normal fluctuations that must occur in the plate-current stream are filtered or bypassed to ground by C9 so that the plate current will be essentially a pure DC in its upward flow through R14. The filter current, which flows up and down through C9 at whatever signal frequencies are being amplified, is shown in dotted blue.

The last voltage-divider current (also shown in dotted red) flows upward from ground through R16 and downward through R17 to the 250-volt power supply. By appropriate choice of the

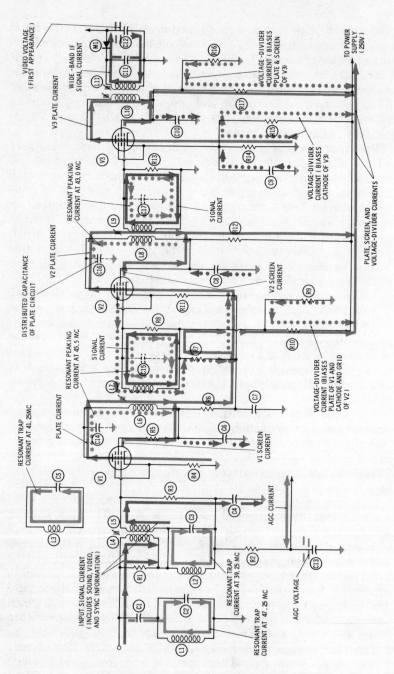

Fig. 4-3. Operation of a three-stage video-IF strip.

sizes of these resistors, a positive voltage of about 175 volts can be developed at their junction and applied to the plate of V3.

All of the plate and screen-grid currents from these three tubes join with the three voltage-divider currents in flowing through the B+ line toward the 250-volt power supply.

Signal Currents

The signal currents that must be amplified by the circuit can have any frequency within the band from 41.25 to 47.25 mc. These signal currents (solid blue) contain the three essential types of information—sync pulses, picture information, and sound information. In addition to carrying important information within the passband, the incoming signal inevitably carries some unwanted frequencies that must be eliminated. These unwanted frequencies include any or all of the following signals:

1. The adjacent-channel sound carrier (47.25 mc).
2. The sound carrier of the channel being received (41.25 mc), usually called the "accompanying" sound carrier.
3. The adjacent-channel picture carrier (39.75 mc).

These unwanted frequencies are eliminated by several actions which emphasize some frequencies and attenuate others. The attenuation processes are accomplished in the resonant-trap circuits at the left of the diagram. Substantial resonant currents build up in each of these three circuits, and feedback actions between the trap circuits and the main input line to the grid of V1 prevent these unwanted frequencies from reaching the grid. As indicated in Fig. 4-3, the three trap circuits have resonant currents in motion at these frequencies:

L1 and C2—47.25 mc (the adjacent-channel sound carrier).
L2 and C3—39.75 mc (the adjacent-channel picture carrier).
L3 and C5—41.25 mc (the accompanying sound carrier).

Each of these trapped currents is shown in solid green. Currents at the remaining frequencies within the passband flow freely up and down through grid-driving resistor R3. The resulting alternating voltage causes relatively large fluctuations in the plate-current stream through V1. These pulsations in plate current develop alternating voltages across the tuned transformer (L6 and L7). Thus, the voltages developed across L6 and L7 are amplified versions of the voltage developed across R3.

The plate-current stream of V2 will have even larger pulsations so that a still larger amplifier voltage is developed across the second tuned transformer (L8 and L9). This same amplifying process will again be repeated by V3. The final IF signal current that flows in the detector tuned circuit (L11 and C11) will have the maximum possible strength for any frequency within the passband. This final IF current is shown in solid blue.

The phenomenon of resonant peaking is utilized in the plate circuits of V1 and V2 to emphasize, or build up, certain frequencies within the passband.

Inductor L6 is chosen so that it resonates with its own distributed capacitance and the interelectrode capacitance of V1 at a frequency of 45.5 mc. These inherent capacitances are shown lumped together as C14. Inductor L8 is chosen so as to resonate with the interelectrode and distributed capacitances in the plate circuit of V2; these capacitances are shown lumped together as C16. Resonance for this combination occurs at a frequency of 43.0 mc. The reader should understand that currents at any frequency within the band of 41.25 to 47.25 mc will flow in these plate circuits, as well as the grid circuits to which they are coupled. However, currents at these two particular frequencies will receive maximum buildup in the respective tank circuits. When the various responses of all the tuned and untuned circuits are taken together, their combined response should approximate the curve of Fig. 4-2.

Currents at these individual resonant frequencies in the plate circuits of V1 and V2 are shown in dotted green. These currents are shown in addition to the wide-band signal current in solid blue. The final appearance of any of these IF currents occurs in the tank circuit (L11 and C11). Currents at any frequency within the passband will build up oscillations of approximately equal strength in this tuned circuit, and each negative half-cycle will force electron current from left to right through detector M1. This unidirectional flow of current will build up an accumulation of electrons on the upper plate of capacitor C12. This accumulation of electrons rises and falls in depth in accordance with the instantaneous strength or weakness of the IF signal current. These changes in depth, or quantity of electrons in storage on capacitor C12, mark the first appearance of the video voltage in the receiver.

The three coupling transformers in this circuit make use of the principle of stagger tuning in that each one is tuned to a different frequency within the IF passband. In addition, one of the transformers (L10-L11) is overcoupled so that resonant peaks of voltage occur on either side of the center frequency. The first three coupling transformers are made up of L4 and L5, L6 and L7, and L8 and L9. These may be identified as "single-tuned" by the single tuning symbol above each set of windings. A transformer which is tuned by a single adjustment for both windings is not generally used in an overcoupled application; instead, it is used for peaking the two coupled circuits to a single resonant frequency within the passband. The resonant frequency for L6 and L7 is 45.5 mc and for L8 and L9 it is 43.0 mc.

Tuning adjustments may be made at these frequencies by applying a signal generator output to the input circuit of tube V1 and observing the response with a VTVM at some later output point. As an example, wtih a signal generator supplying an input signal of 45.5 mc, L6 and L7 may be jointly adjusted with the tuning slug until the voltmeter indicates maximum output. The most likely spot to connect the voltmeter would be across the detector output. Maximum deflection of the voltmeter needle would then indicate that the IF signal current flowing between L11 and C11 would have its maximum strength at the applied frequency of 45.5 mc.

With the signal generator set at 43.0 mc, L8 and L9 should be jointly tuned with the single tuning slug to give maximum deflection of the voltmeter needle. This will indicate a circulating, or oscillatory, current between L11 and C11, flowing at maximum strength at 43.0 mc.

L10 and L11 have separate tuning slugs. This usually identifies a transformer which is deliberately overcoupled for the purpose of achieving the twin resonant peaks. Such peaks contribute much to broadening response curves (broadbanding). A different kind of test is made with this type of transformer. It is necessary to supply two types of signal input—a sweep generator which provides a band of signals perhaps 10 megacycles wide and covering the entire IF band of 41 to 47 mc, and another set of signals known as marker frequencies. These marker frequencies should be 41.25 and 45.75 mc and may be applied separately. The signal from the sweep generator should by itself produce the classic video response curve of Fig. 4-2. Each one should produce a mark or "pip" at the indicated spot on Fig. 4-2. When these marks appear at the indicated points (downhill from the brow of each curve), it is an indication that the passband of the IF strip approaches its desired shape or width. Joint adjusting of the tuning slugs for L10 and L11 should be carried out in order to achieve just the proper degree of tight coupling, assuring the correct bandwidth. Of course, the adjustments for the other transformers can also be made using the sweep generator and oscilloscope. If these instruments are used, the actual effect on the overall response can be seen, and all tuning slugs can be adjusted to obtain the desired response of Fig. 4-2.

Miscellaneous Filter Currents

The three power-supply decoupling currents (dotted blue) flow through the filter capacitors (C6, C8, and C10) at each and every signal frequency passing through the respective tubes. A decoupling current is shown moving downward onto the upper plate of C6, driving an equal number of electrons out of the lower plate and into ground. A decoupling current is being drawn out of the upper plate of C8, drawing an equal number of electrons upward from ground into the lower plate. Finally, a decoupling current is flowing onto the upper plate of C10, driving electrons away from the lower plate and into ground. Each of these decoupling currents accomplishes the same important function, preventing current pulsations at any signal frequency from flowing further along the B+ line and entering the power supply.

A cathode-filter current flows up and down through C9 at whatever signal frequency is being amplified by V3. In Fig. 4-3 it is shown flowing upward onto the lower plate of C9. The movements of this current serve to smooth out the voltage at the cathode of V3, thereby preventing degeneration or loss of amplification.

REVIEW QUESTIONS

1. Is the principle of series peaking, as used in this chapter, for the purpose of increasing or decreasing signal strength? At how many different frequencies in Fig. 4-1 is series peaking used?

2. How many times is shunt peaking used in Fig. 4-1, and at what frequencies?

3. How many distributed capacitances are actually used for tuning purposes in the three-stage Video IF strip of Fig. 4-1?

4. What are the two principle effects of bridging a resistor across a resonant circuit?

5. At what point in Fig. 4-1 does the video voltage make its first appearance? Is this video voltage an alternating voltage, a pulsating negative voltage, or a pulsating positive voltage?

6. In a decoupling filter combination such as that represented by C6 and R8 in Fig. 4-1, assume that the screen current coming from the tube is momentarily *increasing* in quantity. Will the instantaneous current between the lower plate of C6 and the ground flow down or up at this time? How about when the screen current is momentarily decreasing?

7. What two general principles are usually followed when designing tuned circuits to have a particular bandwidth? In the average circuit diagram, how can we identify inductors which are meant to be stagger tuned? How about those which are meant to be overcoupled?

Chapter 5

VIDEO AMPLIFICATION

There are three important functions that must be performed by the video circuitry of a TV receiver. They are:

1. Amplification of the entire video signal present at the video detector output. These signals include the synchronizing and blanking pulses, the picture information, and the FM sound signal.
2. Separation of the three types of signals and delivering them to the sync separator, picture tube, and sound IF amplifier circuits.
3. Selection and application of the appropriate biasing voltages to the cathode and grids of the picture tube.

VIDEO AMPLIFIER

The actions in a video amplifier circuit are given in Fig. 5-1. The signal and biasing circuits for the picture tube are also included in this diagram. The circuitry and actions diagrammed in Fig. 5-1 are typical of those in present-day TV receivers.

Identification of Components

The following components perform the indicated functions in the circuit of Fig. 5-1.

L1, L2—Series peaking inductors for improving high-frequency response.

L3—Shunt peaking inductor, also used to improve high-frequency response.

L4—Part of plate tank which resonates at 4.5 mc.

L5—Inductor for coupling 4.5-mc signal to sound portion of receiver.

L6—Shunt peaking inductor.

L7—Series peaking inductor.

C1—Part of resonant tank that delivers amplified IF signal to video detector M1.

C2, C3—Part of series peaking networks which assists L1 and L2 in providing high-frequency compensation.

C4—Distributed capacitance which resonates with L3 at higher video frequencies to provide the shunt peaking function.

C5—Cathode-bypass capacitor for V1.

C6—Part of plate tank which resonates at 4.5 mc.

C7—Capacitor for coupling 4.5-mc signal to sound system.

C8—Blocking and coupling capacitor between L4 and L5.

C9, C11—Part of contrast-control circuitry.

C10—Decoupling capacitor between contrast control and 105-volt source.

C12—Distributed capacitance which resonates with L7 to provide series peaking (high video-frequency compensation).

C13—Coupling and blocking capacitor between video amplifier and picture-tube cathode.

C14—Large electrolytic capacitor used for decoupling between picture-tube cathode and 255-volt source.

R1, R2—Part of shunt peaking network along with L3 and C4.

R3—Series grid resistor used for isolation.

R4—Cathode-biasing resistor for V1.

R5—Part of voltage-divider network that biases sync separator tube (not essential to the operation of video amplifier).

R6—Video amplifier plate-load resistor.

R7—Variable resistor used as contrast control.

R8—Decoupling resistor to 105-volt source and part of voltage-divider network which determines V1 plate voltage.

R9—Resistor that broadens the response of series peaking inductor L7.

R10, R11, R12—Cathode-biasing resistors for picture tube. (Also function as cathode-driving resistors.)

R12, R13—Voltage-divider network for providing initial positive bias to picture-tube cathode. R12 also serves as brightness control.

R14—Grounding or "return" resistor for control grid of picture tube. (Also functions as a grid-driving resistor for the blanking pulses during retrace actions.)

R15, R16—Voltage-divider network for providing positive voltage to second grid (screen or accelerating grid) of picture tube.

R17—Voltage-dropping resistor for focusing grid of picture tube.

R18—Variable potentiometer used as focus control.

R19—Noise-limiting resistor used in coupling signal to sync separator and noise-limiter stages.

M1—Crystal (diode) detector for demodulating the IF signal delivered by the video-IF amplifier stages.

V1—Sharp-cutoff pentode used as video amplifier.

V2—Cathode-ray tube (picture tube).

Identification of Currents

The following electron currents (identified by the colors indicated) will flow in the circuit of Fig. 5-1 during receiver operation:

1. Plate and screen-grid currents through video amplifier tube V1 (solid red).
2. Electron-beam current (plate current) through picture tube (also in solid red).
3. Screen- and focus-grid currents from picture tube (also in solid red).
4. Wide-band video signal (solid blue).
5. Video-IF current (dotted blue).
6. Shunt- and series-peaking currents at higher video frequencies (also in dotted blue).
7. Noise pulse current (dotted green).
8. Sync pulse current (also in dotted green).
9. 4.5-mc FM audio-carrier current (solid green).
10. Cathode-filter or bypass current for V1 (dotted red).
11. Five separate voltage-divider currents (also in dotted red).

Details of Operation

The video signal makes its first appearance in a television receiver at the output end of the video detector (M1, in Fig. 5-1). Either the diode section of a vacuum tube or a solid-state diode may be used to accomplish the detector functions. The cathode of M1 is the element on the left, and the anode is on the right (represented by a broad arrowhead). The direction of electron flow through any diode can only be from cathode to anode; therefore, the video signal current (solid blue) flows from left to right through M1 in a series of rapid pulsations. These pulsations occur at the video intermediate frequencies. The video current (dotted blue) is flowing back and forth between C1 and L8. These components are chosen to resonate across the video IF band; the resulting current charges C1 alternately to positive and negative voltage peaks. When the upper plate of C1 is positive, M1 is prevented from conducting because its cathode is more positive than its anode. However, when the upper plate of C1 is negative, as it is in the instantaneous picture of Fig. 5-1, a pulsation of electron current will be driven through M1 from left to right. This action will repeat itself more than forty million times each second, since it will occur once during each cycle of the IF.

This unidirectional diode current delivers electrons to the upper plates of C2 and C3, and consequently builds up the negative voltage, known as the video voltage, on these capacitors. This video voltage will leak continuously to ground through inductors L1, L2, and L3 and resistors R1 and R2. This continual drainage, or leakage, is essential to prevent the accumulation of so many electrons (negative voltage) on the upper plates of C2 and C3 that M1 and V1 would be biased so negatively that they would not conduct at all. The leakage process is regulated, or controlled, by the sizes of virtually all of the circuit components involved (C2, C3, C4, L1, L2, L3, R1, and R2). The amount of voltage in storage on C2 and C3 will be proportional to the strength of the incoming IF signal.

The incoming signal at a television antenna is both amplitude and frequency modulated (at different frequencies within the allocated bandwidth). Since the video-IF signal which arrives at the video detector input is the same as the incoming signal in all respects except frequency, it is also modulated in amplitude as well as frequency. The voltage pool that appears on the upper plates of C2 and C3 must reflect or reproduce the amplitude modulation from the video-IF signal. This voltage must have its greatest negative value during those short periods (normally about 5 microseconds) when a synchronizing pulse is being received. These pulses, which are carried at the basic video IF of 45.75 mc, occur every 63.5 microseconds during the presentation (trace-out) of a single horizontal field of 262.5 horizontal lines of picture information on the cathode-ray tube.

Sync and Blanking Signals

The amplitude of the sync pulse which rides on top of the horizontal blanking pulse is not of particular importance in the video amplifier circuit. However, it must be faithfully reproduced so that it can be coupled to the sync separator stage. The entire

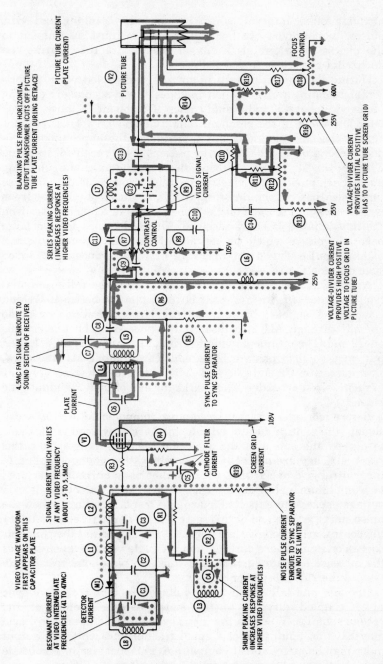

Fig. 5-1. A typical video amplifier and picture-tube circuit.

blanking pulse interval, which includes the blanking and sync pulses, is of importance because this pulse must be coupled to the picture tube circuit to cut off the picture tube during the horizontal retrace period.

During the approximately 10-microsecond period when a horizontal blanking pulse (which includes the sync pulse) is being received, about 450 individual cycles of resonant IF current flow back and forth in the resonant tank (C1 and L8). This resonant current has its maximum strength during the approximately 5-microsecond period that the sync pulse is being received. Its value will be almost as great during the remainder of the blanking pulse. Each pulsation of electron current through M1 during these times also has maximum strength. Thus, an excess of electrons is delivered into storage on the upper plates of C2 and C3 during the time a pulse is being received. These electrons form a large negative voltage which we can identify as a horizontal sync and blanking pulse. This point marks the first appearance of the video sync pulse in the receiver.

As soon as the carrier signal which carries the pulse modulation is turned off, the resonant current flowing between C1 and L8 must disappear. In addition, the large pulsations of diode current through M1 also disappear. The accumulated electrons on C2 and C3 continue flowing to ground through L1, L2, R1, etc.; but since no electrons are being *added* from diode M1, the negative voltage on C2 and C3 is discharged to ground (zero voltage) in relatively short order. This marks the end of the individual sync pulse.

Before considering the remaining components of the video signal (the picture and sound information), it will be worthwhile to discuss the action of the sync and blanking pulses from this point on. They are normally the most negative voltage applied to the control grid of V1; thus the amplifier plate current is reduced to a minimum value during this period. This reduction in grid voltage causes the expected sharp rise in plate voltage when the pulse starts. At the end of this same pulse (10 microseconds later) the control grid becomes less negative, the amplifier tube conducts correspondingly more current, and the plate voltage must drop as the increase in plate current flows through plate-load resistor R6 toward the 255-volt power supply.

One rise and fall of this plate voltage becomes a positive sync pulse coupled directly to the sync-separator section of the receiver via R5. Whereas the input sync pulse at the control grid may have an amplitude of a small fraction of a volt, the output pulse may be many volts in amplitude. This increase in amplitude is due to the amplifying properties of the tube. Amplification is accomplished because a small change in grid-voltage releases (or withholds) a large flow of plate-current electrons; these variations in plate current develop correspondingly large voltage changes across output load resistor R6.

The positive blanking pulse is also coupled to the cathode of the picture tube (V2) via all of the components between the amplifier and the picture tube (i.e., C9, C11, R7, L7, R9, C12, and C13). It is essential that current through the picture tube be completely cut off during the blanking pulse period. The application of the positive pulse to the picture-tube cathode helps to accomplish this objective. The picture-tube cathode is already biased with a positive voltage of perhaps 30 or 40 volts, whereas the first control grid is connected to ground (0V) through R14. Thus, any positive increase in cathode voltage increases the disparity between the cathode and grid voltages and thereby reduces or cuts off the flow of the picture-tube current.

The positive pulse voltage at the cathode is further aided in its function of cutting off the picture tube by a negative blanking pulse from the horizontal output transformer (not shown here). This blanking-pulse current (shown in dotted green) is driven *downward* through grid resistor R14, thereby creating a negative voltage at the control grid of the picture tube. This negative blanking voltage occurs in unison with the positive pulse at the cathode. Fig. 5-1 also shows the positive pulse current being drawn *upward* through R10, R11, and R12. These two actions occur just prior to each sync pulse so that the plate current through the picture tube is cut off for about 10 microseconds. At the end of the pulse period, both currents reverse in direction, thus removing, or eliminating, the biasing conditions which cut off the electron beam through the picture tube. The picture tube is then ready to be turned on in accordance with the varying modulation caused by the picture information.

Noise Pulse Current

An additional current path is provided in this receiver for feeding noise-pulse currents (when they occur) to a special noise-limiter circuit. A noise-pulse current (shown in Fig. 5-1 in dotted green) leaves the detector output and flows downward to the noise limiter in the sync-separator section of the receiver. In flowing through R19, it develops a negative voltage at the top of this resistor which effectively cuts off all plate current through V1. Thus, the voltage at the plate of V1 will rise very quickly toward the maximum plate-supply voltage provided at the upper terminal of R6. This rise in voltage is coupled to the cathode of the picture tube so that the picture tube cuts off for the duration of any such noise pulse. A noise pulse occurring during picture reception will, therefore, cause a dark spot or a dark streak in the picture; however, these spots or streaks are usually not noticeable because of their short duration. A pulse 1-microsecond wide would cut off the picture-tube beam for that period, which is about one-fiftieth, or 2%, of the time required to trace out a single line of picture information.

The Picture Signal

After a sync pulse and its pedestal voltage have passed, the strength of the resonant current in C1 and L8 decreases considerably; however, it will vary from cycle to cycle in accordance with the relative degree of whiteness desired at each particular spot in the single line of picture information being received. Thus, M1 will conduct varying amounts of electrons from cycle to cycle, and the accumulation of electrons on C2 and C3 will vary from cycle to cycle. This accumulation of electrons is the negative video voltage. It causes a pulsating DC to flow downward through R1 and R2 (and L3) toward ground. The resulting voltage developed across these resistors by this pulsating current is the grid-driving voltage for video amplifier V1.

Each small pulsation of video voltage is amplified considerably by the tube action causing large variations in the plate current flowing through load resistor R6. These variations in plate current cause larger variations in the voltage at the upper terminal of this resistor. These variations, which are the amplified video voltage, are then coupled via C9, C11, etc., to the cathode of the picture tube.

The quantity of electrons in the electron beam of the picture tube is proportional, at any instant, to the amount of light, or whiteness, desired at that particular spot on the picture-tube face. The phosphorescent face of the picture tube always exhibits a degree of illumination proportional to the quantity of electrons striking it. Thus, a strong electron beam causes a bright spot (very white) on the picture-tube face. A weak beam causes a faint spot (gray rather than white) to appear on the picture tube screen.

The video signal is shown in solid blue in Fig. 5-1. In the detector portion of the circuit it is a unidirectional current flowing only from left to right through M1 and downward through R1 and R2 to ground. These electrons re-enter the detector circuit by flowing upward from ground into L8.

In the circuit areas to the right of the video amplifier the video signal has again become an alternating current; it flows in two directions through the entire coupling network (C9, C11, R7, L7,

C12, C13, and R9) and the cathode driving network (R10, R11, and R12). At the instant shown in Fig. 5-1, video current is flowing upward and to the left through these networks, creating a positive signal voltage at the picture-tube cathode. This positive video voltage persists for as long as the picture information in that line is desired to be gray or black. (The more positive this voltage becomes, the darker the reproduced spot will be; conversely, the less positive the voltage, the lighter the spot becomes. Hence, all shades of gray can be reproduced.) When a white spot is desired in the picture, a near maximum negative video signal is required. When the video signal becomes negative, the electron currents in the coupling and driving networks reverse direction. Now the flow is to the right and downward. Thus a negative voltage is applied to the cathode, and the electron beam is increased, or turned up.

The video voltage is successfully transferred from the input circuit (the detector) to the output circuit (cathode of the picture tube) by means of pulsations in the plate current of the video amplifier tube (V1). This plate current is shown in solid red, but it is not an easy matter to draw a picture of these pulsations. All of the pulsations must eventually flow downward through R6 toward the 255-volt power source. In doing so, the all-important voltage variations at the top of R6 are developed. These voltage changes then drive electrons in and out of C9 and C11; these electrons become the new video signal current.

Shunt and Series Peaking

Two examples of resonant peaking being used to improve the response to higher video frequencies are shown in Fig. 5-1. L3 is used as a "shunt peaker," and L7 is a "series peaker." The principle involved in each instance is the same. There is a sufficient amount of inherent capacitance between the windings of any inductance to create a condition of resonance at some particular frequency. L3 and L7 are carefully wound during construction so as to possess both the desired amount of inductance and the necessary inherent capacitance. Thus resonance will occur near the high end of the video-frequency band (in the vicinity of 4 mc). Any video signals near this frequency will excite an oscillation of electrons at its own frequency. Two such oscillations are shown in dotted blue; one is flowing upward through L3 and charging inherent capacitance C4 to a negative voltage. This negative voltage is in addition to the particular video voltage at that same frequency which set up the oscillation in the first place. The resonant voltage which will have a greater amplitude than the video voltage which excited it, is applied to the control grid of V1 through

R1 and R3. Therefore, greater amplification, or response, of the higher video frequencies will be provided by V1.

This process is called high-frequency compensation. It is made necessary by the fact that all circuit components, including amplifier tubes, have a certain amount of inherent, or built-in, capacitance to ground. Since it is the nature of any capacitance to pass a high-frequency current more easily than a low-frequency current, the higher video frequencies are shunted to ground. It is necessary to compensate for this undesirable phenomenon by providing greater circuit response to the higher frequencies. R2 and R9 are placed in parallel with compensating inductors L3 and L9 for the purpose of broadening their response over a wider frequency band, even at the expense of considerable gain at their particular resonant frequencies.

The Audio Signal

The audio information carried by the television carrier signal is a frequency-modulated signal centered around a frequency of 4.5 mc above the video carrier. This FM signal, which varies as much as 25 kc on either side of the center frequency, is amplified only slightly in passing through the tuner and video-IF amplifier sections of the receiver. It is delivered to the detector input simultaneously with the synchronizing signals and the picture information.

Several important characteristics of the picture, synchronizing, and sound signals—their relative sizes (amplitudes), frequencies, and sequencing—are given in Fig. 5-2. Line 1 of this illustration shows the audio signal; this signal is of relatively small amplitude, and the amplitude is constant or unchanging. Close inspection of this line will reveal that the frequency of this signal is constantly changing.

Line 2 of Fig. 5-2 shows a typical single line of picture information. The individual cycles of electron oscillation (shown in blue) are occurring at the basic picture-carrier frequency or at any of the associated sideband frequencies. The modulation envelope has been drawn from peak to peak of the individual cycles. The sideband frequencies may extend upward to 4 mc above the carriers, but they should stop short of the portion of the band reserved for the FM audio signal.

Line 3 of Fig. 5-2 shows the IF carrier as it is modulated by the so-called "blanking pedestal" and a horizontal synchronizing signal. When the sync signal is being received, no picture information is being transmitted or received. The sync signal has a greater amplitude than even the strongest part of the picture signal. The strongest part of the picture signal is that part which completely turns off the cathode-ray tube and portrays a black portion of the picture. When the sync signal is made stronger than this, it assures that the cathode-ray tube will also be cut off during the period of each sync signal. Since the sync signal always coincides with the beam-retrace action, the greater strength of the sync pulse carrier assures that the electron beam through the picture tube will be turned off during retrace.

Be sure you can relate the waveforms of Fig. 5-2 to the several currents and/or voltages depicted in Fig. 5-1. The individual cycles that make up the carrier waveforms in Lines 2 and 3 correspond to the electron current (solid red) which flows back and forth between L8 and C1 as a resonant current. Each negative half-cycle of this carrier forces electron current to flow through detector M1 from left to right. The strength, or amplitude, of each of these half-cycles determines the *amount* of electron current which will be forced through the detector. This instantaneous signal strength will always be accurately reflected in the quantity of electrons accumulated in the voltage pool on the upper plates of C2 and C3. This accumulated voltage is sometimes referred to as the "detector" voltage, but it is also the video voltage which alternately provides synchronizing signals to the sync separator and picture signals to the cathode-ray tube.

The resonant current (shown in dotted blue) flows between C1 and L8 and contains the frequency-modulated audio signal carrier whose waveform is shown in Line 1 of Fig. 5-2. Since this is a low-amplitude signal, it is always "masked" by the stronger sync and picture-carrier signals. This masking action is important because it insures that the electron voltage on C2 and C3 will always reflect or reproduce the amplitude or strength of the sync and picture carriers only. It must not be increased by any additional diode conduction resulting from the FM sound carrier. This is one of the reasons why the sound carrier is held at a much lower level than the lowest picture carrier strength (white level).

Each negative half-cycle of the sound carrier inevitably causes diode M1 to conduct some small amount of electrons, but since each half-cycle has the same strength as all other half-cycles, a small fixed component of negative voltage is added to the voltage on C2 and C3 and becomes, in effect, part of the bias voltage for V1.

While these actions are going on, additional pulsations of current flow through diode M1 at the video-carrier frequency of 45.75 mc, as well as at each one of the video sidebands. Two very important mixing processes occur as a result of these simultaneous current actions. The FM carrier frequency, which is centered around 41.25 mc, mixes, or beats, with the picture-carrier frequency of 45.75 mc, producing a sound-IF signal centered around the new frequency of 4.5 mc. Since the original FM sound signal had deviations of ±25 kc imposed on it, the new IF sound signal will also have these same deviations, so the sound-IF band will be from 4.475 to 4.525 mc. The tuned plate circuit (C6 and L4) is resonant at this center frequency of 4.5 mc. As the resonant tank current (solid green) flows up and down through L4, it in-

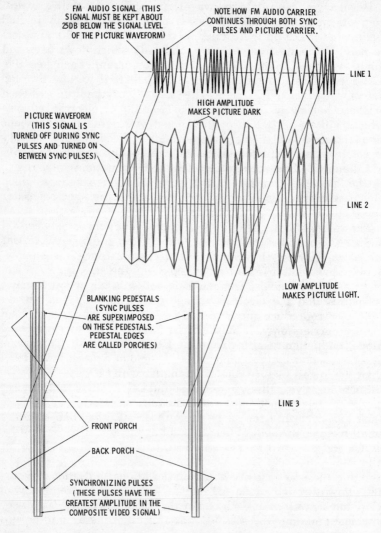

Fig. 5-2. Phase and amplitude relationships of the sync pulse, picture, and audio components of the composite video signal.

duces a companion current, flowing in two directions through L5. This current drives electrons in and out of C7, which couples this driving action to the sound-IF amplifiers.

The other important process that occurs in the video detector circuit involves the picture-carrier frequency of 45.75 mc and all of the video sidebands. These sidebands may extend as much as 4 mc above the picture carrier. When the video-IF frequency is removed, frequencies from zero to 4 mc result. These frequencies become the video (picture) signal. They are amplified by V1 and pass downward through L4 to an eventual junction with R6, C9, and C11. There they are coupled to the cathode of the picture tube.

Voltage-Divider Currents

There is a total of five different voltage-divider currents which flow continuously in the circuit of Fig. 5-1. These currents are all essentially pure DC; they are almost always used to provide fixed values of positive voltage for application to the various electrodes of vacuum tubes. Such voltage values are usually called baising voltages, meaning that they bias a tube electrode to a particular operating voltage. One of the virtues in identifying all of the voltage-divider currents in any circuit under study is the large number of circuit resistors which can be explained as "voltage-divider resistors." The function they perform (providing reduced values of positive voltage for application to various tube electrodes) is technically a power-supply function. Normally, a power supply will provide only one or two values of high positive voltage, each having considerable current-carrying capacity. The circuit designer can then construct voltage dividers at any point in the receiver where a paritcular value of voltage is needed.

The first of the voltage-divider currents has its origin in the sync-separator circuit (not shown). This current is drawn upward through R5 and then downward through R6 and L6 to the 255-volt source. In addition to providing a low positive voltage at some point in the sync-separator circuit, it provides a higher value at the upper terminal of R5; this voltage becomes the plate-supply voltage for video-output tube V1. The amount of this plate-supply voltage is also affected by the second voltage-divider current which flows upward through R8 and R7 and then downward through R6 and L6 to the 255-volt point. This current originates at a 105-volt tap in the power supply.

R7 is the contrast control for the receiver. It can be used to vary the amount of output from the video amplifier that is actually coupled to the cathode of the picture tube. For example, if the variable tap on R7 is positioned directly opposite the fixed tap that leads to C9, the output signal is not required to flow through any portion of R7 on its way to the picture tube. Thus, maximum gain is being attained from the amplifier. If, however, the variable tap is moved upward or downward on R7, then the output signal which is being coupled through C9 must also flow through a portion of R7 and suffer some attenuation or loss. The entire video waveform will be proportionately attenuated by this adjustment. This attenuation tends to make dark spots or objects in the picture less dark and white spots or objects less white. Maximum contrast clearly implies achieving the maximum possible gain or output from the video output tube, thus providing a video voltage waveform with the largest possible swings between light and dark spots. The subject of picture contrast will be considered in greater detail when the brightness-control function is discussed.

The video voltage is coupled to the picture tube through two parallel capacitive paths—C9 and C11. C9 is the larger of the two; therefore most of the signal flows through it. Whenever part of the contrast control (R7) is interposed in the path through C9, the total impedance of this path is increased so C9 carries a smaller portion of the signal voltage and C11 carries a larger portion.

The third voltage-divider current flows upward from ground through R12 and R13 toward the 255-volt source. R12 is a variable resistor that serves as the brightness control, a front-panel operator adjustment which controls the bias on the picture tube. (A typical value provided by this variable resistor is 50 volts). The special relationship between this cathode-voltage value and the relative brightness of the picture tube will be discussed later.

The fourth voltage-divider current flows upward through R15 and downward through R16 to the same 255-volt source. The resulting voltage at the junction of the two resistors (about 50 volts) is applied to the screen grid of the picture tube. This voltage serves as an accelerating voltage to accelerate the plate-current stream of electrons flowing through the picture tube.

The final voltage-divider current flows from ground through R18 toward the high positive voltage known as B+ boost. In this receiver it has a value of +600 volts. The principle by which B+ boost voltage is achieved has been considered at length in a companion text of this series, *TV Sync and Deflection Circuits*. R18 is another variable resistor which serves as a focus control. The voltage which is tapped from R18 is applied to one of the electrodes of the picture tube to concentrate (focus) the electron stream through the tube so that it will strike the face of the picture tube in as small a point or area as possible. A typical value for the focus electrode voltage in this receiver is 400 volts.

BRIGHTNESS CONTROL AND DC REINSERTION

Fig. 5-3 shows a standard circuit diagram of an older-type TV receiver. It employs a principle known as DC reinsertion for adjusting the brightness (brilliance) of the picture tube when confronted with varying degrees of incoming signal strength. In simplest terms, the purpose of this circuit was to provide the picture tube with a value of operating grid-bias voltage which would equal the value of the pedestal or blanking voltage in the video signal itself. This gave assurance that any lesser value of video voltage would cause some electron flow through the picture tube and some degree of whiteness in the picture. While the principle of DC reinsertion using a diode tube is seldom encountered in modern receivers, an understanding of this function may help one to understand how it can now be omitted from receiver design.

In Fig. 5-3, a video waveform having negative sync pulses is delivered at the output of V1. The plate current through this tube (solid red) will flow at its maximum rate when sync pulses are being received and amplified. As this plate current flows downward through the plate-load circuit (L2 and R2), it develops the voltage drop, which causes the plate voltage to become low when maximum current flows. As each pulsation of plate current (which represents a negative sync pulse) flows through the tube, it drives electrons onto coupling capacitor C1 and downward through resistors R4 and R7 to ground. This action develops a negative voltage at the cathode of diode V2, causing electron current (solid blue) to flow through the diode from cathode to plate. The complete path for these electrons is through the diode from cathode to plate where they enter ground, then out of ground and upward through R7 to the cathode.

This one-way flow of electron current through V2 creates an electron deficiency on the right-hand plate of C2. This electron deficiency, which in reality is a positive voltage (indicated by the blue plus signs), is applied to the control grid of the picture tube as a biasing voltage. The frequency of the sync pulses is 15,750 cycles per second, but the time constant of the R7 and C2 combination is very long compared to the time of one cycle—perhaps a fiftieth or a hundredth of a second. Thus, the charge (voltage) formed on the right-hand plate of C2 will be preserved for a hundred or so sync pulses.

The value of the positive voltage on the right-hand plate of C2 depends on two factors: the strength of the sync pulses at this point, and the size of R4. If R4 had zero value (if it were a short circuit, in other words), the cathode of V2 would have the full value of the negative sync pulse applied each cycle. Then electrons would leave the cathode and cross to the plate in such a quantity that the electron deficiency created on C2 would be a positive voltage exactly equal to the value of the sync pulse voltage. For example, if the negative sync pulse coming from the video amplifier has an amplitude of −50 volts, then C2 would charge to +50 volts. This 50 volts would be applied to the control grid of the picture tube as a biasing voltage to establish a reference value from which the smaller video variations could be measured. The brightness control (variable resistor R5) must be set so that a positive voltage will be applied to the cathode, ensuring that the negative sync pulses will cut off the picture tube. When this is done, any given amplitude of picture signal will always release the same quantity of electrons through the picture tube and thereby produce the same degree of whiteness on the picture-tube face. The foregoing can only be achieved if the varying video voltages carrying the picture information are measured from the same reference point, namely, a grid-cathode voltage that is equal to total darkness of the picture tube. Any value of grid voltage more positive than this blanking voltage will cause some illumination of the picture tube.

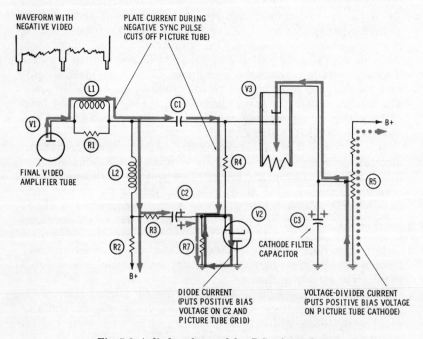

Fig. 5-3. A diode tube used for DC reinsertion.

A single half-cycle of the video driving voltage (solid red) is shown flowing downward through R4 and R7 to ground. If this flow is large, a high value of negative voltage will be developed at the top of R4 and at the control grid of the picture tube. This component of negative voltage acts in opposition to the positive biasing voltage on the right-hand plate of C2; therefore, the amount of picture-tube current flowing at that particular instant will be reduced. This causes one small spot on the picture tube to be unilluminated, or to have only slight illumination; a black or gray spot results.

A half-cycle later the driving current will be drawn upward through R4 and R7, developing a component of positive voltage which adds to the positive biasing voltage on C2 and leads to a white or light gray spot on the picture tube.

A corollary function but one of equal importance which was provided by the DC reinsertion circuit was that of cutting off the picture tube during retrace actions. As explained previously, when the cathode-biasing voltage is properly adjusted by voltage-dividing resistor R5, the driving current associated with the large negative sync pulse will flow downward through R4 and R7 in sufficient quantity to develop a negative cutoff voltage at the grid of the picture tube.

Elimination of DC Reinsertion

Very few receivers marketed in recent years include a special tube circuit for accomplishing the objective formerly known as DC reinsertion. This objective might be stated as an attempt to insure that the background light levels associated with various portions or elements of a picture are consistently measured or gauged from the same standard of light or darkness. This standard, called the black level, is determined by the blanking or pedestal level on which the sync pulse sits. This objective has not been realized in its entirety by the newer circuitry, but it has been attained to a satisfactory degree. Fig. 5-1 illustrates one typical example. The output waveform of video voltage from V1 is coupled eventually through C13 to the cathode of picture tube V2. The picture tube is cathode-driven, as are almost all picture tubes in modern receivers. The picture-tube driving current (solid blue) flows up and down through R10, R11, and R12 between C13 and ground. Downward excursions of this current develop a negative voltage at the upper terminal of R10 and at the cathode of the picture tube. This negative cathode voltage causes an increase in picture-tube current. The upward excursion of driving current through these resistors places a positive voltage on the cathode of V2 and restricts the amount of picture-tube current.

The largest amount of picture-tube current flows when the cathode is driven to its most negative (or least positive) voltage values. Much smaller quantities flow when the video voltage at the cathode has its higher positive values. Thus, positive excursions of video voltage tend to reduce the picture-tube current and cause dark or gray spots on the screen, while negative excursions cause white or light spots in the picture.

All of the picture-tube current must flow upward through R12, R11, and R10 before reaching the tube. In so doing, an additional component of positive biasing voltage is developed. This voltage must be added to the permanent biasing voltage created by the voltage-divider current flowing through brightness control R12. In other words, the positive cathode voltage at the picture tube is the sum of two voltages, a fixed voltage of about +50 volts due to voltage-divider action in R12 and a variable amount of self-bias which always results when a tube plate current must flow through a resistive path before reaching the cathode.

As with all cathode voltages resulting from self-bias, the amount of this voltage must change when the amount of tube current changes. If the cathode is not bypassed by a filter capacitor, degeneration or loss of signal strength results. Whenever the signal causes an increase in plate current, the cathode voltage rises in the positive direction; this increase in cathode voltage, in turn, *reduces* the plate current. When the cathode resistor (or resistors) are bypassed by a filter capacitor, a means exists for smoothing out the cathode voltage so that instantaneous variations in plate current through these resistors will not cause instantaneous voltage variations at the cathode.

The length of time that a filter capacitor will hold or retain a voltage depends on the RC time constant of the combination. In Fig. 5-1 the total capacitive path which contributes to the filtering action at the cathode of V2 would include C13, L7, part of R7, and C10. C10 is much smaller than C13, and the total capacitance of two capacitors in series must always be less than the capacitance of the smallest one. The time constant of R10, R11, and R12 in combination with C13, C10, etc., will be on the order of 25 microseconds, or about half of the time duration of a single line of picture information.

When the background of a picture being received is predominantly gray or dark, the total picture tube current will be considerably less than for a light or white picture. Therefore, for the predominately gray picture, the cathode will have a lower positive voltage on it. When a steep negative dip in the video signal occurs, denoting a white spot on the picture, it drives the cathode voltage from this lower base or average value. This causes the white spot to appear somewhat whiter than it should, and the lowered cathode voltage causes the gray background to be somewhat less gray than it actually is.

When a picture background is predominantly white, the total picture-tube current over a period of time is obviously larger than normal. This increases the positive self-bias on the picture tube. The first result is a slight decrease in the tube current which generates the whiteness, and a decrease in the shade of whiteness. A gray or dark object in the midst of this light background will be made to appear more dark (more gray), because a positive video pulsation of any size does not have as far to go to reach the total blackness or cutoff point, since it starts from a higher base, or higher cathode voltage.

It is emphasized that this circuit does not accomplish the same function as DC reinsertion in the older circuits. Elimination of DC reinsertion from modern receivers represents a compromise which was made in order to eliminate one additional tube (such as the diode V2 in Fig. 5-3) from the receiver, thereby saving a small amount of cost. There is a definite loss in fidelity of the picture, because the varying shades of white and gray are not reproduced exactly as they appear in the studio. This loss in picture fidelity is rarely noticeable to the viewer, and the compromise must be considered to have passed the test of usage and customer acceptance.

REVIEW QUESTIONS

1. The paragraph title "Identification of Currents" on page 83 lists 11 different currents, all of which are shown in Fig. 5-1. For each of these, state whether they are pure DC, pulsating DC, or true alternating currents.

2. In all systems for receiving *modulated signals*, there is an identifiable point at which the modulated waveform makes its first appearance, usually in the form of a voltage. In Fig. 5-1, where is this point and what is the name of the waveform?

3. Where do the units of electric charge (electrons or ions) come from and what circuit components lie in their discharge path to ground?

4. In the typical TV signal, is the picture information transmitted continuously or intermittently? How about the sound informa-tion? Why is it necessary to periodically interrupt one of these signals, but not the other?

5. Why, in your opinion, is it desirable to cut off the picture beam during the retrace action? In Fig. 5-1, describe the biasing and driving actions which together accomplish this function.

6. Describe the circuit action by which a received noise pulse is used to momentarily cut off the picture tube.

7. Describe the circuit actions which result in generation of a totally new frequency—the Sound IF. Where does this frequency first appear? Is the Sound-IF an AM or an FM signal?

8. Trace the separate paths of each of the voltage-divider currents which are used to provide variable adjustments to the picture tube in Fig. 5-1.

Chapter 6

TV SOUND SYSTEMS USING GATED-BEAM AND LOCKED-OSCILLATOR– QUADRATURE-GRID DETECTORS

The sound systems employed in TV receivers are usually classified according to the type of detector circuit employed. In this chapter two circuits, the gated-beam and locked-oscillator–quadrature-grid detectors, will be discussed. Both of these circuits employ similar principles of operation. A stage of 4.5-mc amplification usually precedes the detector circuit. However, because of the self-limiting feature of these circuits, the IF amplifier stage may be eliminated. Because of the high-level output from these circuits, no voltage amplifier is required; usually only a single stage of power amplification follows the detector.

GATED-BEAM FM DETECTOR

Fig. 6-1 shows the principal circuit action occurring in a circuit using a gated-beam type of detector. This circuit appears only occasionally in modern receivers, but its principles of operation reappear in a more popular adaptation, which will be discussed later. The gated-beam circuit requires a special tube.

Identification of Components

This gated-beam detector circuit includes the following functional components:

L1—Plate-load inductor for V1.

L2—Secondary winding of transformer in output circuit of V1.

L3—Inductor portion of resonant quadrature circuit at second control grid of V2.

L4—Primary winding of audio-output transformer.

L5—Secondary winding of audio-output transformer.

L6—Speaker winding.

C1—Decoupling capacitor between V1 plate circuit and power supply.

C2—Resonant tank capacitor.

C3—Neutralizing capacitor between output and input circuits of V1.

C4—Neutralizing capacitor between screen grid and input of V2.

C5—Screen-grid decoupling capacitor for V2.

C6—Resonant-tank capacitor in quadrature circuit.

C7—Detector output capacitor.

C8—Coupling and blocking capacitor.

C9—Cathode-bypass capacitor for V3.

C10—Screen-grid decoupling capacitor for V3.

C11—RF bypass capacitor.

C12—Tone-control capacitor.

R1—Grid-driving resistor for sound-IF amplifier V1.

R2—Plate-decoupling resistor for V1.

R3—Cathode-biasing and "buzz-control" resistor for V2.

R4—Small resistor used for feedback purposes to quadrature circuit.

R5—Screen-grid dropping resistor for V2.

R6—Plate-load resistor for V2.

R7—Tone-control resistor.

R8—Volume-control resistor.

R9—Cathode-biasing resistor for V3.

R10—Decoupling resistor between V3 plate and power supply.

V1—Sound-IF amplifier tube.

V2—Gated-beam detector tube.

V3—Beam-power audio-amplifier tube.

Identification of Currents

The following electron currents flow in this circuit during normal operation:

1. Grid-driving current for sound IF amplifier V1 (solid blue).
2. Plate currents through each of the three tubes (solid red).

3. Screen-grid current through V2 and V3 (dotted red).
4. Resonant signal currents in two tank circuits (also in solid blue).
5. Audio tone-control current through R7 (solid green).
6. Grid-driving current through volume-control resistor R8 (also in solid green).
7. Speaker driving current through L5 and L6 (also in solid green).
8. Power-supply decoupling currents through C1 and C10 (also in dotted red).
9. Screen-grid filter current through C5 (also in dotted red).

Details of Operation

The important functions which must be performed by an inter-carrier sound system such as this one include:

1. Amplification and limiting (or leveling) of the 4.5-mc frequency-modulated sound carrier.
2. Detection or demodulation of the frequency-modulated signal without responding to any variations in signal amplitude surviving the limiting process.
3. Amplification of the resulting audio-frequency signal to the point where it can drive a speaker.

Most modern receivers are intercarrier types, meaning the frequency-modulated sound carrier is carried through all stages of the video-IF amplifier strip, and passed through the second, or video, detector. This signal may also be passed through the video amplifier or video-output stage, before being filtered away from the picture signal and passed to the sound section of the receiver. In Fig. 6-1, the sound signal (solid blue) is being driven downward through grid-driving resistor R1. This signal current flows back and forth between R1 and the video amplifier at an instantaneous frequency which must be within 25 kc of the 4.5-mc center frequency (between 4.475 and 4.525 mc, in other words).

V1 functions as a conventional amplifier tube operated under Class-A conditions; its plate current (solid red) flows continuously and pulsates each time the grid is made positive by the upward movement of signal current through R1. These pulsations in plate current flow downward through L1 and induce an alternating current to flow up and down through secondary winding L2. Inductor L2 and C2 constitute a tuned tank circuit which resonates at the 4.5-mc center frequency. This circuit cannot be sharply resonant, because any signal within the band of 4.475 to 4.525 mc must be passed.

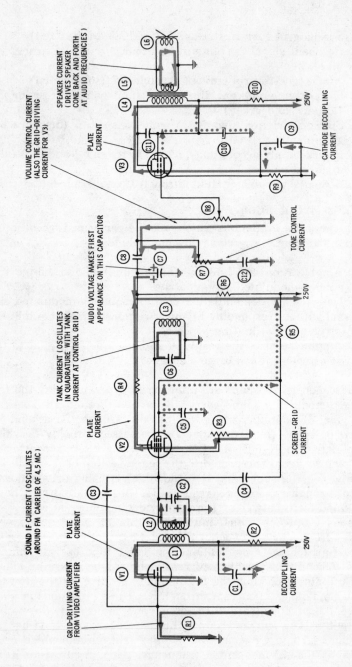

Fig. 6-1. Operation of a typical sound system employing a gated-beam
FM detector circuit.

Broadening the response curve of a tuned circuit is normally accomplished by placing a resistor across it. No such resistor is used here, but the same effect can be accomplished in the coupling process. Primary winding L1 is considered to be in parallel with the internal resistance of V1; thus an equivalent portion of this resistance is coupled to the tuned tank. Details of this type of coupling action are difficult to portray pictorially; however, the desired widening of the tuned-tank response curve, with an attendant loss in gain, results.

The second grid of V2 serves as a control grid. The oscillation of electrons between L2 and C2 periodically makes this control grid positive so that a pulse of electron current is released through the tube. On alternating half-cycles of this tank voltage, the grid is made negative enough to cut off the plate current entirely. As each pulsation of plate current passes the fourth grid, it induces a small current flow in the second tank circuit (L3 and C6). This is a sharply tuned circuit which is also resonant at the 4.5-mc center frequency. The induction of current reoccurs once each cycle, setting up and sustaining an oscillation of electrons in the tank circuit. The oscillation is said to be "in quadrature" with the

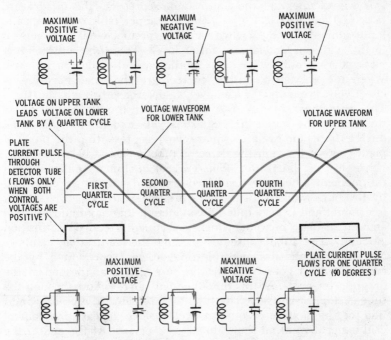

Fig. 6-2. Five successive quarter-cycles in the operation of two resonant tanks which are in quadrature with each other.

first oscillation. This means that the two oscillatory voltages are 90° out of phase with each other. The oscillation in the second tank (L3 and C6) "leads" the oscillation in the first tank by a quarter of a cycle, meaning that it will achieve a positive voltage peak a quarter of a cycle in advance of the first oscillation.

V3 is so constructed and biased that it requires a relatively small voltage swing on either control grid to drive the tube between the two extremes of cutoff and saturation. This feature assures that the tube will function as a limiter, since limiting results whenever any amplitude variations of the signal can be rendered ineffective in controlling the flow of plate current through the detector tube. Fig. 6-2 shows the current movements and associated voltage peaks in two tuned tank circuits operating 90° out of phase with each other—in other words, in quadrature. The voltage in the upper tank reaches a positive peak at the start of the first quarter-cycle, indicated graphically by the positive peak in the waveform. The voltage in the lower tank reaches its positive peak 90° later, at the start of the second quarter-cycle, as indicated by the blue waveform. Thus the red waveform leads the blue waveform by a quarter of a cycle.

If we assume that the lower tank represents the quadrature tank (L3 and C6) of Fig. 6-1 and the upper tank represents the input tank (L2 and C2), we can then predict what will happen to the plate-current stream through V2. This tube will conduct plate current only when *both* of the control grids are positive. When the voltage on either control grid becomes negative, it effectively prevents the passage of electrons through the tube. The waveforms in Fig. 6-2 indicate that this condition exists throughout the entire first quarter-cycle *and at no other time* during the whole cycle. A square wave representing the pulse of plate current through the detector tube is shown below the sine waves in this illustration. This current is shut off entirely until the moment when the second control-grid voltage (represented by the blue waveform) becomes positive. Then the tube begins to conduct and is very quickly conducting the maximum possible amount of plate current, which is frequently called "saturation current." The tube continues passing this saturation value of current until the first control-grid voltage (represented by the red waveform) goes from positive to negative at the end of the first quarter-cycle. At this time the plate-current flow through the tube is stopped entirely. The tube then remains in a cutoff condition for the next three quarter-cycles, since at least one control grid is negative at all times during this period. At the end of the fourth quarter-cycle, both control grids are positive again, and the tube once again conducts plate current.

All of this plate current must eventually flow downward through load resistor R6 to the 250-volt B+ source. Before it can enter this resistor, however, it accumulates on the upper plate of C7. This accumulation results in a somewhat lower positive voltage existing on C7 than would otherwise exist. In the prolonged absence of any plate current through V2, the upper plate of C7 would charge to the power-supply voltage (250 volts). The time constant of the RC combination (C7 and R6) is made large enough so that C7 will not discharge electrons through R6 in any significant quantity during the short interval between plate current pulses. The result is that under the conditions described, the voltage on C7 is essentially a DC voltage.

The preceding conditions occur only in the absence of any frequency modulation of the sound carrier. Both oscillations are occurring exactly at the 4.5-mc center frequency, and the quarter-cycle phase difference between the two oscillatory voltages is fairly accurately maintained.

Phase Shifts When Modulation Is Present

When the incoming sound carrier is frequency-modulated by audio information, the phase relationship between the two oscillating tank voltages will be significantly altered. When the IF signal goes below the center frequency, the voltage in the quadrature tank moves closer to an in-phase condition with the voltage in the input tank. This condition is depicted in Fig. 6-3, which shows five successive current/voltage pictures in the tuned circuits. Each picture represents an eighth of a cycle, so the five pictures cover only one-half of a cycle rather than an entire cycle, as they did in Fig. 6-2. The upper tank, which represents the input tank circuit (L2 and C2), achieves its positive peak voltage at the start of the second eighth of a cycle. This positive peak is indicated by the plus signs massed on the upper plate of the capacitor, and by the red waveform. One-eighth of a cycle later, the lower tank, which represents the quadrature tank, achieves its positive peak of voltage. This is indicated by the plus signs massed on the upper plate of the tank capacitor and by the blue waveform.

Since the two waveforms are now closer to being in phase with each other, the period of time when they are both positive is increased from a quarter of a cycle to three-eighths of a cycle. This period begins when the blue waveform becomes positive at the left-hand side of Fig. 6-3, and it ends when the red waveform crosses the zero line and becomes negative. Since each tank is connected to a control grid of V2, this tube will conduct a longer pulse of plate current than when the tanks are exactly in quadrature. Thus, a greater quantity of electrons flows as plate current under these conditions, and these electrons accumulate on the upper plate of C7, causing a lower positive voltage to exist at this point. The long time constant of C7 and R6 preserves this low positive voltage from cycle to cycle for as long as the input signal current frequency is below the center frequency.

When the IF signal goes above the center frequency, the instantaneous phases of the two oscillatory tank voltages move farther apart (Fig. 6-4). The upper tank achieves its positive voltage peak

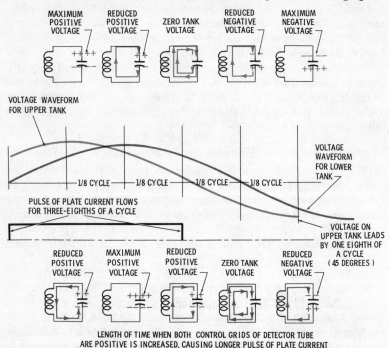

Fig. 6-3. Current movements during a half-cycle in two tanks whose voltage phases are less than a quarter-cycle apart.

at the start of the first one-eighth of a cycle. This is indicated by the plus signs on the upper plate of the capacitor and by the red waveform. The lower tank voltage is negative at this instant; it does not become positive until an eighth of a cycle has elapsed. Both tanks are then positive for one-eighth of a cycle; it is only during this shortened time period that plate current is permitted to flow through V2. The shortened pulse of plate current is shown below the colored waveforms. This pulse represents a reduced quantity of plate current electrons which will be delivered to the upper plate of C7. As long as the input frequency remains above the center frequency, the time-duration of the plate-current pulses will be shortened, and the result is that the positive voltage on C7 will increase.

By varying the signal frequency above and below 4.5 mc, we have a means of varying the positive voltage on the upper plate of C7. There are two important characteristics of an FM signal voltage which can be used to carry audio information. These characteristics are the rate of the frequency excursion, and the amount of the frequency excursion. An *excursion* in carrier frequency is defined as the number of cycles or kilocycles per second by which the carrier is made to differ from the center frequency. When the excursion of a carrier frequency is very slight (perhaps only a few hundred cycles), the resulting change in phase between the input voltage and the quadrature voltage will also be slight, and the amount of electron current contained in the plate-current pulses will vary over a small range. This small variation in current, in turn, causes small variations in the positive voltage that accumulates on the upper plate of C7.

The voltage on C7 marks the first appearance of the audio signal in the receiver. A very weak audio sound will result when the voltage variations on C7 are small, as in the preceding example.

If the signal frequency varies above and below the center frequency by large amounts (perhaps by 10 or 20 kc), the successive amounts of electron currents contained in the plate-current pulses will vary over a much wider range. These variations in plate-current pulses, in turn, will cause wider variations in the positive voltage on the upper plate of C7. A strong or loud audio signal will be the result. Thus, we see that the *loudness* of an audio signal depends directly on the *amount* of the FM-signal frequency excursion.

The *pitch* of an audio signal depends on the *rate* at which the frequency excursions of the carrier are made to occur. For example, if the carrier signal is made to vary above and below its center frequency 100 times per second, then the pitch of the resultant audio voltage which appears on C7 will be 100 cycles per second. The positive voltage on C7 will rise and fall at this rate. It will rise when the shortened pulses of plate current (Fig. 6-4) are flowing, and fall to a lower positive value when the longer pulses of plate current flow (Fig. 6-3).

As a result of these fluctuations in the positive voltage on C7, an audio current will be driven up and down through parallel resistors R7 and R8. In Fig. 6-1 these currents are being drawn upward. This might be termed a positive half-cycle; it would occur during a period when shortened pulses of plate current are flowing through the detector tube. Negative half-cycles of audio will occur when the lengthened pulses of detector current flow. The audio current (green) would then flow downward through R7 and R8. R8 functions as the volume control. By adjusting this resistor, the listener can tap off any desired portion of the audio signal for amplification by the audio-output circuit constructed around V3.

R7 and C12 constitute a tone-control device. This device enables the listener to eliminate some signal strength of the higher-frequency tones in the audio without a comparable attenuation of the lower-frequency sounds. If the variable tap on R7 is lowered to its lowermost position, most of the high-frequency tones will flow in and out of C12. Thus, the high-frequency tones are by-passed to ground, rather than flowing through the somewhat higher impedance offered by R8. The lower-frequency currents in the audio signal find the reactance of C12 to be much larger than the resistance of R8, so these currents flow up and down through R8 in a normal fashion and develop an audio voltage across the resistor.

If the variable tap on R7 is moved to its uppermost position, then both the high-frequency and the low-frequency currents in the audio signal will be confronted by equal amounts of this resistance so that the high-frequency tones will be attenuated less *with respect to the low-frequency tones* than before.

When wide variations in adjustment of R7 are made, it may be necessary to readjust the volume control (R8) to maintain the same sound level from the speaker. The reason is that, as the total impedance of the R7-C12 combination increases, more and more of the total audio current being driven through the two paths is diverted through R8, and less flows through R7 and C12. Thus the audio voltage developed across R8 is increased. Also, when the tone-control adjustment is moved downward on R7 (decreasing the resistance), more of the total audio current flows through it at the expense of that current which develops the audio-output voltage across R8.

R3 in the cathode circuit of V2 is called a buzz control. Its purpose is to adjust the gain of the detector and to eliminate the possibility of amplifying some portion of the horizontal-sync signals that may have survived the various filtering and limiting actions. Sync signals and other noise will not be heard unless the incoming signal strength drops to the point where it does not drive the detector tube to saturation. If the tube is not driven to saturation, the limiting function cannot be carried out.

The plate current through V3 pulsates at the audio frequencies. As this current flows downward through L4 it induces an alternating current to flow up and down through secondary winding L5. This current becomes the speaker current (solid green). As this current flows back and forth through the speaker winding (L6) it causes the speaker diaphragm to vibrate at these same audio frequencies, thus reproducing the desired sounds.

In order to prevent the gated-beam circuit from feeding energy back from output to input and thereby oscillating, a specially constructed tube is used for V2. The input control grid is surrounded by a shielding grid. This grid is connected to the positive power supply through R5; therefore, it will attract considerable electron current within the tube. This current (dotted red) flows through R5 toward the power supply. The shielding provided by this grid prevents the oscillatory voltage in the quadrature tank from being "sensed" in the control-grid circuit. Instead of this happening, the shielding grid intercepts these voltage impulses and bypasses them harmlessly to ground via C5. This capacitor also filters the pulsations from the screen current so that electrons flow through R5 in a steady stream. This filtering action assures that the voltage on the shielding grid will be maintained at a constant value.

Feedback through the interelectrode capacitance between tube elements is used to strengthen the oscillation in the quadrature tank. R4 is a low-value resistor (a few hundred ohms) in the plate circuit of the tube. Its function is to develop a small component of voltage at the plate each time a pulse of plate current comes through the tube. A small component of voltage (negative at the plate side) is developed across this resistor with the passage of each pulse of plate current. Each such component of negative voltage at the plate is sensed at the quadrature grid, and it occurs in appropriate phase to reinforce the oscillation occurring between L3 and C6. This is not the only source of support or replenishment for this oscillation, since it is also sustained by an induction process from the plate current electron stream as it pulsates through the tube. This coupling process occurs as the electron stream passes the second control grid (quadrature grid) and is usually referred to as electron coupling.

LOCKED-OSCILLATOR–QUADRATURE-GRID DETECTOR

Fig. 6-5 shows a widely used FM detector which embodies many of the principles of the gated-beam detector. This circuit is called a locked-oscillator–quadrature-grid detector, abbreviated LO-QG. The name is derived from the fact that the tuned circuits associated with V2 cause this circuit to oscillate, and the oscillation fre-

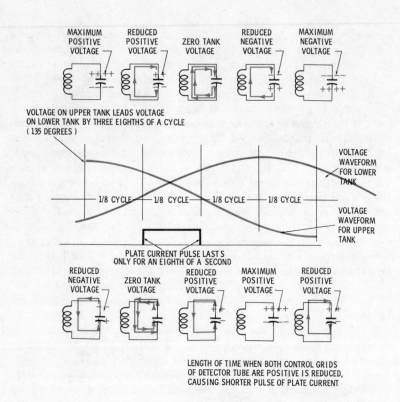

MAXIMUM POSITIVE VOLTAGE — REDUCED POSITIVE VOLTAGE — ZERO TANK VOLTAGE — REDUCED NEGATIVE VOLTAGE — MAXIMUM NEGATIVE VOLTAGE —

VOLTAGE ON UPPER TANK LEADS VOLTAGE ON LOWER TANK BY THREE EIGHTHS OF A CYCLE (135 DEGREES)

VOLTAGE WAVEFORM FOR LOWER TANK

— 1/8 CYCLE — 1/8 CYCLE — 1/8 CYCLE — 1/8 CYCLE —

VOLTAGE WAVEFORM FOR UPPER TANK

PLATE CURRENT PULSE LASTS ONLY FOR AN EIGHTH OF A SECOND

REDUCED NEGATIVE VOLTAGE — ZERO TANK VOLTAGE — REDUCED POSITIVE VOLTAGE — MAXIMUM POSITIVE VOLTAGE — REDUCED POSITIVE VOLTAGE —

LENGTH OF TIME WHEN BOTH CONTROL GRIDS OF DETECTOR TUBE ARE POSITIVE IS REDUCED, CAUSING SHORTER PULSE OF PLATE CURRENT

Fig. 6-4. Current movements during a half-cycle in two tanks whose voltage phases are more than a quarter-cycle apart.

quency is controlled, or locked, by the instantaneous frequency of the FM sound signal.

Identification of Components

This circuit is made up of the following functional components:

L1—Primary winding of sound IF transformer.
L2—Secondary winding of sound IF transformer.
L3—Inductor portion of quadrature tuned-tank circuit.
C1—Capacitor portion of sound IF tuned-tank circuit.
C2—Capacitor portion of detector grid tuned-tank circuit.
C3—Screen-grid filter capacitor.
C4—Capacitor portion of quadrature tuned-tank circuit.
C5—Filter capacitor between quadrature tank and ground.
C6—Audio-output capacitor.
C7—Coupling and blocking capacitor to V3.
R1—Cathode-biasing resistor for V1.

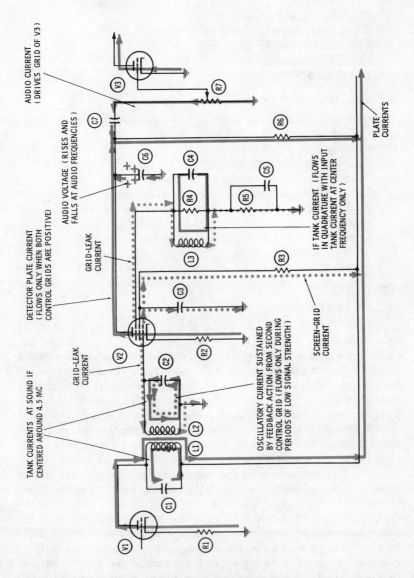

Fig. 6-5. Operation of a sound circuit employing a locked-oscillator–quadrature-grid detector.

113

R2—Cathode-biasing resistor for V2.

R3—Screen-grid dropping resistor for V2.

R4—Broadbanding resistor across quadrature tank circuit.

R5—Biasing and isolating resistor between quadrature tank and ground.

R6—Plate-load resistor for V2.

R7—Grid-driving and volume-control resistor.

V1—Final sound-IF amplifier tube.

V2—FM detector tube.

V3—Audio-output tube.

Identification of Currents

The following electron currents flow in this circuit during normal operation:

1. Three plate currents through the three tubes (solid red).
2. Screen-grid current through V2 (dotted red).
3. Three FM signal tank currents (solid blue).
4. Audio current through volume-control resistor R7 (solid green).
5. Leakage current from first and second control grids of V2 (dotted green).
6. Weak signal oscillating current in tank L2 and C2 (dotted blue).

Details of Operation

Amplifier tube V1 is driven by the FM sound signal from the video amplifier. This driving action causes the plate current to pulsate through V1 and to set up an oscillation of electrons (solid blue) in the first tank circuit. By virtue of the transformer action between L1 and L2, a second oscillatory current (also shown in solid blue) will be set up and maintained between C2 and L2. This current alternately places a positive and a negative voltage on the upper plate of C2, and this voltage turns the detector tube on and off so that pulses of plate current flow through it. Each such pulse of current induces a small voltage in the tuned circuit (L3 and C4) connected to the second control grid. These pulses are sufficient to set up an oscillation at the same frequency between L3 and C4. The resonant frequency of all three tank circuits (L1-C1, L2-C2, and L3-C4) is the same—4.5 mc. Therefore, this frequency becomes the center frequency of the sound-IF passband. When the sound FM signal is exactly at this frequency (corresponding to no modulation and no audio) the oscillation between L3 and C4 will be exactly in phase quadrature with the oscillation in input tank L2 and C2.

When the input signal frequency varies above and below 4.5 mc, the relative phases of the oscillations in the two tank circuits (control grid and quadrature grid tanks) vary in the same manner as described previously for the gated-beam detector circuit. The result is that the quantity of plate current which flows through V2 decreases when the signal goes above the center frequency, and it increases when the signal goes below the center frequency. This happens because when the two oscillations move closer to an in-phase condition, which happens below resonance, V2 conducts for a longer period during each cycle. When the phases of the two oscillations move farther apart, as they do above resonance, V2 conducts for shorter periods during each cycle. The waveforms of Figs. 6-2, 6-3, and 6-4 can be used with equal validity for this circuit as well as for the gated-beam detector discussed previously.

The term "locked oscillator" is derived from the fact that this circuit oscillates due to feedback from quadrature circuit to input circuit. This becomes important in fringe areas where the sound signal is very weak, because the feedback process builds up an oscillation in the input circuit at whatever frequency the sound signal exhibits. Without an input signal, the circuit will not oscillate. There is coupling due to interelectrode capacitance between the first and second control grids. When a fairly strong signal is received, the first control grid is driven positive enough to draw some grid-leakage current from the tube. This current (dotted green) flows out of the tube and downward through L2 to ground. These successive pulsations of grid-leakage current come out of the tube when the grid tank is at its most positive voltage; since these leakage electrons are negative, they reduce or dampen the strength of the positive tank voltage to such an extent that the input tank circuit will not oscillate under these conditions. It should be remembered that there are essentially *two* types of oscillatory current which can flow in the tank circuit (L2 and C2). The current shown in solid blue is a resonant current which is sustained in oscillation by transformer action between L1 and L2. This current is a result of the pulsations in V1 plate current through L1 caused by the signal.

The other oscillatory current in this tank is shown in dotted blue. This current comes into existence only when the input signal strength coupled between L1 and L2 is very weak. This current is sustained in oscillation by feedback from the second control grid, which is connected to the quadrature tank circuit (L3 and C4). During the reception of weak signals, the combined circuit functions as a true self-sustained oscillator. The quadrature tank is maintained in oscillation by the passage of individual pulsations of plate current which are released into the tube by the oscillating voltage at the input tank (L2 and C2). This input tank is maintained in oscillation by feedback (through the tube interelectrode capacitance) from the second control grid to the first control grid.

During weak-signal operation the signal voltage coupled from L1 to L2 is small, but it is enough to assist the oscillation in the tank. In particular, it regulates its frequency so that the tank will always oscillate at the instantaneous frequency of the IF sound signal, which may vary between 4.475 and 4.525 mc. Thus it can be said that a weak sound signal *synchronizes* the oscillating detector to the sound frequency, and the self-sustaining oscillator delivers the equivalent of a strong sound-IF signal despite the basic weakness of the incoming signal.

As the incoming signal improves, or strengthens, grid-leakage current begins to flow into the first control grid, nullifying the effect of the feedback impulses coming from the quadrature grid. The self-sustained nature of the oscillation then disappears, and the resonant current (dotted blue) drops out of oscillation. The

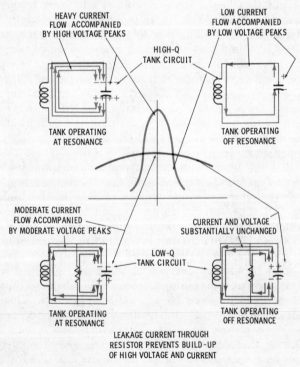

Fig. 6-6. Comparison of sharp and broad response curves.

oscillatory current (solid blue) continues to flow in the tuned tank; it is sustained, or supported, by transformer action between L1 and L2. Since the signal strength has now increased, the transformer action is strong enough so that the resonant current and voltage in L2 and C2 will be sufficiently strong. V2 will be driven to conduct saturation current on the positive voltage peaks, so the necessary limiting action of the tube will be achieved.

In this circuit, as in the gated-beam detector, either of the two control grids must be able to cut off the flow of plate current through the tube. This is accomplished by conventional biasing techniques for the two grids. Cathode resistor R2 provides a small amount of positive bias between the cathode and the first control grid. The second control grid is biased by resistor R5, which is very large—about 500,000 ohms. It is inevitable that some electron current will strike the wires of this grid within the tube and flow out of the tube as a grid-leakage current. In flowing downward through R5, this leakage current (dotted green) develops a small negative voltage at the upper terminal. This becomes the biasing voltage around which the grid voltage is varied by the resonant tank voltage.

The screen-grid current (dotted red) flows in fairly large quantity because of the high positive voltage of the screen grid. It is drawn steadily downward through R3 toward the power supply. Since the plate current is going through the tube in pulsations, the screen-grid current will exit from the tube in pulsations, but the pulsing characteristic will be filtered to ground by C3. This filter current flows downward onto C3 and into ground, as shown in Fig. 6-5, when the screen current first leaves the tube. A moment later, at the end of the current pulse through the tube, the screen current decreases and then stops. This causes the filter current to reverse its direction, and it flows momentarily upward onto the lower plate of C3, being drawn upward by the attendant rise in positive voltage in the screen area.

HIGH- AND LOW-Q CIRCUITS

Fig. 6-6 shows typical response curves of a high-quality (high-Q) and a low-quality (low-Q) resonant circuit. The two resonant tanks above and below these curves are intended to typify the two types of circuits. In the high-Q circuit (shown at the top) a heavy electron current flows when the circuit is operating at resonance; this builds up large negative and positive voltage peaks across the tank capacitor. However, when the tank is operated somewhat off its resonant frequency, as indicated in the right-hand diagram, the quantity of electrons in oscillation drops off considerably, and the peak voltages developed across the tank capacitor are reduced accordingly.

In the circuit at the bottom of Fig. 6-6, a resistor is bridged across the tank circuit, making it a low-Q circuit. Here, the current or voltage cannot build up to the values shown in the upper left diagram. Whenever the voltage begins to build up across the capacitor, electrons will be driven from the negative side to the positive side, flowing through the resistor. In the lower-left drawing, electrons are shown flowing downward through the resistor, because a negative voltage peak has accumulated on the upper plate of the tank capacitor. As long as there is *any* amount of negative voltage on the top plate of the capacitor, electrons will be driven down through this resistor.

The advantage of using the low-Q circuit is that when it is operated at frequencies off resonance, the proportionate reduction in quantity of electrons in oscillation is much less than in the high-Q circuit. This is indicated in the lower right-hand tank circuit of Fig. 6-6. The result is a response curve that is much flatter than that of the high-Q circuit.

REVIEW QUESTIONS

1. In the quadrature oscillation occurring between L3 and C6 (Fig. 6-1), describe how each individual cycle is replenished or sustained.

2. What two separate voltages determine when V2 (Fig. 6-1) will conduct? What must the phase relationship be between these two voltages in order for the tube to conduct?

3. When the carrier frequency deviates *below* the center frequency, do the two tank oscillations move closer together or farther apart in phase? When this happens, does V2 conduct more electrons, or fewer electrons?

4. When the positive voltage on the upper plate of capacitor C7 becomes *more* positive, is it a sign that the oscillations in the two tanks have moved closer together or farther apart in phase? Would this indicate a frequency deviation above or below the center frequency?

5. What is the principal function of a tone control, such as the combination of R7 and C12 in Fig. 6-1? In adjusting the variable resistor arm on R7, in which direction should it be moved—up or down—to provide maximum attenuation or reduction of the higher audio frequencies?

6. What is the function of a buzz control? Which component in Fig. 6-1 provides this function?

7. The quadrature oscillation in the second tuned tank must be isolated from the oscillation in the first tank so that energy will not be fed back to the first tank. What constructional feature of the tube assures that this isolation will exist?

8. In the locked oscillator-quadrature detector circuit of Fig. 6-5, does grid-leakage current from V2 flow on weak signals, strong signals, or both? When it does flow, how does it affect the oscillation (shown in dotted blue) in the grid tank?

Chapter 7

TV SOUND SYSTEMS
USING RATIO DETECTORS
AND DISCRIMINATORS

The audio detector circuits discussed in the preceding chapter
are the most popular circuits in modern TV receivers. However,
in the past, the ratio detector and Foster-Seeley discriminator circuits enjoyed wide usage. They will still be encountered in some
present-day sets and many older sets still in use have one of these
circuits.

A dual-diode tube (or two crystal diodes) is employed as the
audio detector in both of these circuits. While the 4.5-mc audio-
IF amplifier stage may be omitted in some receivers with a gated-
beam or locked-oscillator–quadrature-grid detector, it is always
used in receivers with one of the detectors described in this chapter. In fact, two such stages, with the final stage acting as a limiter,
are often employed. (A limiter stage is essential with the discriminator circuit.) In addition, because the diodes do not provide any
gain, a stage of voltage amplification will be added between the
detector and the audio power output stage.

RATIO DETECTOR

A complete sound system utilizing a ratio-detector circuit for
the demodulation of the frequency-modulated sound carrier is
given in Fig. 7-1. As mentioned in the preceding, this circuit has
been largely supplanted by one of the quadrature detectors discussed in Chapter 6. The principal disadvantage of the ratio de-

tector, when compared to the circuits in Chapter 6, is insufficient output strength; additional amplifier stages are required after the detector.

Identification of Components

This circuit is made up of the following components which perform the indicated functions:

L1, L2—Sound-IF amplifier output transformer.
L3—Tertiary winding to provide quadrature coupling from V1 plate circuit to detecting diodes.
C1—Cathode-bypass capacitor for V1.
C2—Power-supply decoupling capacitor.
C3—Capacitor portion of resonant tank circuit.
C4—Audio-output capacitor.
C5—Electrolytic capacitor across biasing resistor R5.
C6—High-frequency filter capacitor across R5.
C7, C8—Audio-coupling capacitors.
C9—Coupling and blocking capacitor.
C10—Cathode-bypass capacitor for V4.
R1—Grid-driving resistor for V1.
R2—Cathode-biasing resistor for V1.
R3—Plate-decoupling resistor for V1.
R4—Combines with C4 as a long time-constant network to audio-output frequencies.
R5—Initial biasing resistor for ratio-detector diodes.
R6—Manual volume control.
R7—Grid-driving resistor for V3.
R8—Plate-load resistor for V3.
R9—Grid-driving resistor for V4.
R10—Cathode-biasing resistor for V4.
V1—Final sound-IF amplifier tube.
V2—Ratio-detector tube.
V3—Audio-amplifier tube.
V4—Audio-output tube.

Identification of Currents

The following electron currents will flow in this sound system during normal operation:

1. Amplifier plate currents for V1, V3, and V4 (solid red).
2. Cathode-filter currents for V1 and V4 (dotted red).
3. V1 screen-grid current (also in solid red).
4. Resonant current through secondary winding L2 (solid blue).
5. Grid-driving current for V1 (also in solid blue).

6. Current induced in tertiary winding L3 (dotted blue).
7. Unidirectional currents through diodes (dotted green).
8. Audio-drive current through C7, R6, C8, and R7 (solid green).
9. Audio-drive current through R9 (also in solid green).

Details of Operation

The principal functions to be accomplished by this sound system can be summarized as follows:

1. Amplification of the frequency-modulated sound signal in the plate circuit of V1.
2. Coupling of this amplified FM signal *by two separate and independent methods* from the plate circuit of V1 to detector diodes V2A and V2B.
3. Unequal conduction of the two diodes, and the resultant development of an audio voltage on the upper plate of C4.
4. Amplification of this audio voltage in the circuits associated with V3 and V4.

The functions performed by the sound-IF amplifier circuit will not be described in detail since they are the same as discussed in the previous chapter.

The grid-driving current (solid blue) is driven from the video amplifier at any frequency within the FM passband of 4.475 to 4.525 mc. It moves up and down through R1 and develops an alternating positive and negative voltage at the upper terminal of this resistor. The instantaneous value of the alternating voltage controls the quantity of electrons passing through the tube as plate current.

The fluctuations in plate current flowing downward through L1 induce an alternating current to flow up and down through secondary winding L2. This alternating current sets up an oscillation of electrons between L2 and C3, which constitute a resonant tank circuit at the 4.5-mc center frequency. The resonant current resulting from this coupling action is shown in solid blue in Fig. 7-1. When the oscillating electrons move to the upper plate of C3 (as indicated in Fig. 7-1), they make this plate (and the plate of V2A) negative. V2A does not conduct electrons during this period. The lower plate of C3 (and the cathode of V2B) will be made positive by this same action; therefore V2B will also be unable to conduct electrons during this period.

A half-cycle later, these oscillating electrons make the upper plate of C3 positive and the lower plate negative, causing the two diodes to conduct equal amounts of electrons. If only this single means of coupling between L1 and L2 were employed, the two diodes would conduct simultaneously once each cycle in equal amounts. Thus, neither a positive nor a negative voltage can accumulate on the upper plate of C4. Varying the signal frequency above or below the 4.5-mc center frequency will not change this fact, because the two diodes are connected to opposite ends of the same resonant tank. The strength of the resonant voltage and current (solid blue) in the tank would change when this detuning action occurs, but the two diodes would still conduct equal amounts of electrons and the net voltage developed on C4 would still be zero.

Momentarily disregard the preceding action and consider the results of the coupling action between L1 and L3 (the tertiary winding). Since L3 is connected to the center tap of L2, the induced voltage polarity at the top of L3 will be applied simultaneously to the plate of V2A and to the cathode of V2B. In Fig. 7-1 a moment when the voltage across L3 is negative is being depicted. Therefore, electrons are driven away from the center tap of L2 in both directions so that they appear to flood simultaneously onto both plates of capacitor C3. The current that carries these electrons is shown in dotted blue.

The resultant negative voltage at the cathode of V2B causes V2B to conduct some electrons (dotted green). Diode V2A is unable to conduct during this half-cycle because of its negative plate. However, in the half-cycle which follows it, the top of L3 is positive. Now electrons will be drawn toward the center tap through both halves of L2. This electron current places a positive voltage on the plate of V2A, causing it to conduct. It also places a positive voltage on the cathode of V2B, causing it not to conduct.

Even though the two diodes conduct on alternate half-cycles (due to the mode of coupling to the center tap of L2), the diodes conduct equal quantities of electrons so that there can be no accumulation of negative electrons or positive ions on the upper plate of C4.

During the normal operation of a ratio detector, both of the coupling actions described in the foregoing are used. When the signal is exactly on the 4.5-mc center frequency, the two diodes will conduct equal amounts of electrons so no voltage can build up on C4. This condition exists when the carrier is unmodulated by any audio signal. When the carrier is modulated, however, the two diodes conduct unequal amounts of electrons so that an audio voltage can be built up on C4. When the carrier frequency goes above the center frequency, V2A conducts more electrons than it does normally, and V2B conducts fewer electrons. This leads to an excess of electrons lodged somewhere between the two diodes; these electrons accumulate on the upper plate of C4 as a negative voltage. This constitutes a negative half-cycle of audio.

When the carrier frequency deviates below the center frequency, the lower diode will conduct more electrons than normal, and the upper diode will conduct fewer electrons than normal. This leads to a deficiency of electrons between the two diodes and manifests itself as a positive voltage on the upper plate of C4. This becomes a positive half-cycle of audio voltage.

The graphs given in Figs. 7-2, 7-3, and 7-4 will explain why the diodes conduct unequal amounts of electrons when the frequency varies on either side of the center frequency. Fig. 7-2 shows sine-wave representations of the voltages that must be considered in analyzing the circuit operation. Fig. 7-2 depicts the conditions at resonance; that is, the incoming signal is at the 4.5-mc center frequency. The four voltages which must be considered are:

1. The voltage applied to V2A by the resonant-tank current.
2. The voltage applied to V2B by this same current.
3. The voltage applied to V2A by the center-tapped coupling method.
4. The voltage applied to V2B by this same method.

For the sake of simplicity, the two types of voltages are assumed to have the same strength, or amplitude. Line 1 shows the two voltages as they are applied to upper diode V2A. The dotted-blue waveform, which represents the voltage coupled to the center tap of L2 by L3, starts the first quarter-cycle at zero amplitude, and increases to its positive peak a quarter of a cycle later. This waveform is in phase with the voltage waveform across L1.

At the start of the second quarter-cycle the solid blue waveform has zero amplitude; it increases to a positive maximum at the end of the second quarter-cycle. The amplitude of this waveform at any instant represents the voltage at the top of the tuned circuit caused by the resonant current (solid blue in Fig. 7-1).

This voltage is displaced by 90° (quarter of a cycle) from the voltage which induces it from L1. It is characteristic of two inductively-coupled tuned circuits that, when operating exactly at resonance, the two oscillating voltages will be exactly a quarter of a cycle out of phase with each other. Then, as the operating frequency varies above resonance, this phase difference decreases. When the operating frequency varies below resonance, this phase difference increases.

The summation of the two applied sine-wave voltages is shown in red in Fig. 7-2. The amplitude of the red waveform in Line 1 at any instant represents the voltage applied to the plate of diode V2A. V2A will conduct whenever its plate is positive with respect to its cathode.

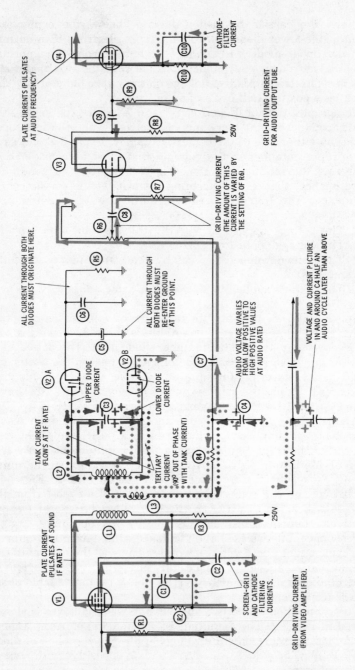

Fig. 7-1. Operation of a sound system employing a ratio detector.

Line 2 (Fig. 7-2) shows the two voltage waveforms applied to the cathode of lower diode V2B and their resultant. The dotted blue waveform, which is the voltage applied from L3 through the center tap on L2, is in phase with the one shown in Line 1, since the upper and lower ends of the tank circuit receive identical impulses from L3. The solid blue waveform is a "mirror image" of its counterpart in Line 1, since this is a measure of the resonant

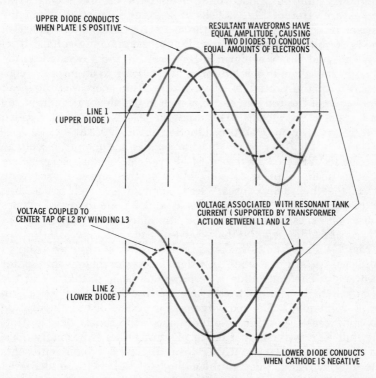

UPPER DIODE CONDUCTS
WHEN PLATE IS POSITIVE

RESULTANT WAVEFORMS HAVE
EQUAL AMPLITUDE , CAUSING
TWO DIODES TO CONDUCT
EQUAL AMOUNTS OF ELECTRONS

LINE 1
(UPPER DIODE)

VOLTAGE COUPLED TO
CENTER TAP OF L2 BY WINDING L3

VOLTAGE ASSOCIATED WITH RESONANT TANK
CURRENT (SUPPORTED BY TRANSFORMER
ACTION BETWEEN L1 AND L2)

LINE 2
(LOWER DIODE)

LOWER DIODE CONDUCTS
WHEN CATHODE IS NEGATIVE

Fig. 7-2. The two input signal waveforms and the resultant applied to each diode when the signal is on the center frequency.

tank voltage. When the top of the tank is positive, the bottom of the tank must be negative, and vice versa. The red waveform is the algebraic summation of these two applied voltages. Whenever the cathode of V2B is made more positive than its plate by these combined voltages, V2B can be expected to conduct electrons.

It can be seen from inspection of the two combined (red) waveforms that they appear to be symmetrical. The positive peak amplitude achieved in Line 1 (and applied to the plate of V2A) appears to equal the negative peak amplitude achieved in Line 2 (and applied to the cathode of V2B). Thus, when a condition of resonance exists, the two diodes will conduct on alternate half-cycles, and they will conduct equal amounts of electrons so that no voltage can accumulate on C4. This is as it should be, because when an FM signal is exactly at its center frequency, it is carrying no modulation.

When the carrier frequency deviates above or below the center frequency, the 90° phase differences between the voltage sine waves are altered. Fig. 7-3 shows a sample situation when the carrier frequency goes above the center frequency. The phase of the tank voltage moves closer to that of the inducing voltage from V1. The solid blue waveform in Line 1 of Fig. 7-3 moves a fraction of a quarter-cycle to the left, bringing it closer to an in-phase condition with the dotted blue waveform. This increases the peak amplitude of the red waveform, which is the algebraic sum of the two applied waveforms. This increase in the resultant applied voltage leads to increased conduction through V2A.

Line 2 of Fig. 7-3 reveals that the peak amplitude of the voltage applied to V2B (red waveform) is decreased, because the negative voltage peaks applied to V2B move farther apart rather than closer together. This causes V2B to conduct fewer electrons than at resonance. The result of this unequal conduction of diodes causes an excess of electrons to accumulate on the upper plate of C4, creating the negative half-cycle of audio voltage.

Fig. 7-4 shows how the phase relationship of the two coupled voltages are altered when the signal deviates below the center frequency. The solid blue waveform has been shifted a fraction of a cycle to the right so that it now lags the dotted blue waveform by more than 90°. The red waveform in Line 1 of this illustration has a decreased positive amplitude above the center line, indicating that V2A will conduct fewer electrons than it normally does. At the same time, the red waveform in Line 2, which represents the total voltage applied to the cathode of V2B, will be increased in amplitude so that V2B will conduct more electrons than it normally does.

As a result of this unequal conduction of the two diodes, a deficiency of electrons will exist on the upper plate of C4; this becomes a positive half-cycle of audio voltage. The peak value of these positive and negative half-cycles of audio voltage will be determined by the amount by which the relative phasing between the two input voltage waveforms (solid and dotted blue, respectively) is shifted. This shift, in turn, depends on the amount by which the carrier frequency deviates from the center frequency. The *amount* of the audio voltage on C4 determines the *loudness* of the sound. The *rate* at which the carrier frequency is deviated above and below the center frequency determines the *frequency* of the audio voltage; thus it determines the pitch of the sound.

Fig. 7-5 shows the significant voltage and current waveforms. They have been shown in color to relate them (where possible) to the waveform colors in Figs. 7-2 through 7-4. These colors are also related somewhat but not entirely to the colors used for particular currents flowing in the detector portion of Fig. 7-1. The six lines and seven columns in this illustration are as follows:

Lines

Line 1—A frequency-modulated carrier signal, such as that which oscillates in tuned tank L2 and C3. The oscillating current in Fig. 7-1 is shown in solid blue, and this companion waveform is also in blue.

Line 2—Voltage waveform applied to plate of V2A as a result of adding the out-of-phase blue waveforms in Line 1 of Figs. 7-2 through 7-4.

Line 3—Individual pulsations of electron current through V2A. They are shown in green to correspond to the color chosen for this current in Fig. 7-1.

Line 4—Voltage waveform applied to cathode of V2B. These cycles represent a culmination of thousands of individual red waveforms from Line 2 of Figs. 7-2 through 7-4.

Line 5—Individual pulsations of electron current through V2B. These are shown in green to correspond with the color chosen in Fig. 7-1.

Line 6—Audio voltage which accumulates on the upper plate of C4 as a result of unequal conduction of the two diodes. This voltage is shown in green to correspond with the color chosen for audio currents in Fig. 7-1.

Columns

Column 1—Waveforms during period of no modulation.

Column 2—Waveforms when carrier frequency deviates above the center frequency. This generates a negative half-cycle of audio voltage.

Column 3—Waveforms when carrier frequency deviates below center frequency. This generates a positive half-cycle of audio voltage.

Column 4—Same as Column 2.

Column 5—Same as Column 3.

Column 6—Same as Column 2, except that a change in carrier amplitude has occurred due to inadequate limiting processes prior to that point. This amounts to un-

wanted amplitude modulation which must be counteracted.

Column 7—Same as Column 3 except for unwanted amplitude
modulation.

Referring to Fig. 7-2, when the two applied voltage waveforms
shown in solid and dotted blue are exactly 90° out of phase with
each other, the resultant red waveforms in Lines 1 and 2 of Fig.

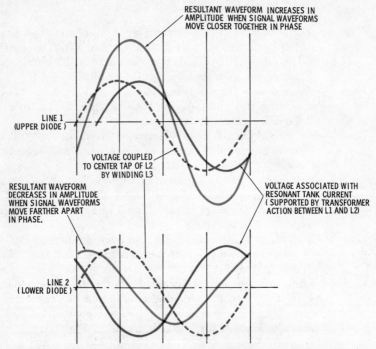

Fig. 7-3. The two input signal waveforms and the resultant applied to each
diode when the signal is above the center frequency.

7-2 have equal amplitude. This condition is illustrated in Lines 2
and 4 of Fig. 7-5, where the individual cycles of all waveforms
in Column 1 are equally spaced, denoting no frequency deviation
or modulation in the applied signal. Every cycle in both red waveforms has the same amplitude or height as every other cycle.
Diode V2A will conduct electrons each time one of the positive
swings of the red waveform in Line 2 makes the diode plate more
positive than the cathode; the amount it conducts is represented
by the height of the individual "pips" or pulses (shown in green
in Line 3).

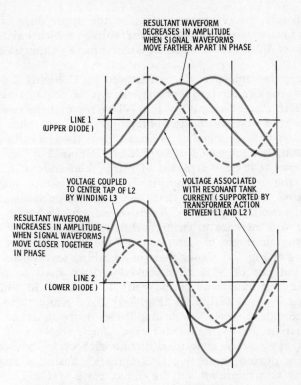

RESULTANT WAVEFORM
DECREASES IN AMPLITUDE
WHEN SIGNAL WAVEFORMS
MOVE FARTHER APART IN PHASE

LINE 1
(UPPER DIODE)

VOLTAGE COUPLED
TO CENTER TAP OF L2
BY WINDING L3

VOLTAGE ASSOCIATED
WITH RESONANT TANK
CURRENT (SUPPORTED BY
TRANSFORMER ACTION
BETWEEN L1 AND L2)

RESULTANT WAVEFORM
INCREASES IN AMPLITUDE
WHEN SIGNAL WAVEFORMS
MOVE CLOSER TOGETHER
IN PHASE

LINE 2
(LOWER DIODE)

Fig. 7-4. The two input signal waveforms and the resultant applied to each diode when the signal is below the center frequency.

Lower diode V2B will conduct electrons each time one of the negative swings of the red waveform of Line 4 makes its cathode more negative than its plate, which is grounded. The amount of electrons it conducts each cycle is represented by the height of the individual green pips or pulses of Line 5. Throughout the time period represented by Column 1 (when the carrier frequency is unmodulated) the red waveforms in Lines 2 and 4 must have the same amplitude; therefore, the green pulsations of current in Lines 3 and 5 must have the same height or strength. This tells us that when a carrier signal is on its center frequency, the two diodes conduct equally; that is, just as many electrons come into C4 from V2A during positive half-cycles of the carrier as go out during negative half-cycles through V2B. This establishes a reference value of audio voltage which becomes the axis, or center line (Line 6 of Fig. 7-5). Its value would be zero volts if the cathode of V2B were grounded. Since the cathode of V2B has a positive voltage on it (caused by current flow upward

129

through R5), the reference voltage on the upper plate of capacitor C4 becomes exactly half of the voltage which exists at the cathode of V2A. An example of such voltage values will be discussed later.

During the time periods represented by Columns 2 and 4 in Fig. 7-5, the carrier frequency speeds up, or deviates above the center frequnecy. In Line 1 of Fig. 7-3 we see that the two voltage waveforms (solid and dotted blue) applied to the plate of V2A have moved closer together in phase. Thus their resultant waveform (red) has increased in amplitude. Column 2 of Line 2 (Fig. 7-5) shows that over a period of many thousands of individual cycles, the resultant waveform is very definitely amplitude-modulated, with the result that the individual pulsations of electron current through V2A (represented by the green pips in Line 3) will increase in strength during these two periods, thus delivering an excess of electrons onto the upper plate of C4.

Line 2 of Fig. 7-3 shows that the two blue waveforms applied to the cathode of V2B have moved farther apart in phase so that the resultant waveform (red) is reduced in amplitude. Columns 2 and 4 of Line 4 (Fig. 7-5) show many thousands of these individual cycles, whose amplitudes decrease as the amount of deviation above the center frequency increases. Thus the amount of electrons conducted during each cycle by diode V2B decreases during these two time-periods, causing a surplus of electrons to accumulate on the upper plate of C4. Since these are the same time periods during which the upper diode is delivering excess electrons onto C4, it can be seen that a negative voltage must build up on C4; this voltage becomes a negative half-cycle of audio voltage (green in Line 6).

When we relate the information shown in Fig. 7-4 to the waveforms in Columns 3 and 5 of Fig. 7-5, we can demonstrate how a positive half-cycle of audio voltage can be accumulated on C4. As the carrier frequency deviates below resonance, the resultant waveform applied to the plate of diode V2A decreases in amplitude, and the resultant (red) waveform applied to the cathode of diode V2B increases simultaneously in amplitude. These actions cause decreased electron flow through the upper diode and increased current through the lower diode, respectively. These combined actions create a deficiency of electrons on the upper plate of C4 which becomes a positive half-cycle of audio voltage. These are depicted in Columns 3 and 5 of Line 6 (Fig. 7-5).

The Limiting Function

It is essential in the demodulation of FM signals that the detector not respond to any amplitude variations in the incoming

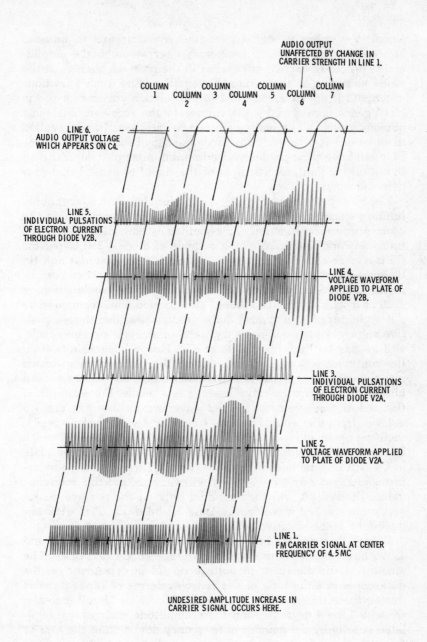

AUDIO OUTPUT
UNAFFECTED BY CHANGE IN
CARRIER STRENGTH IN LINE 1.

COLUMN 1   COLUMN 3   COLUMN 5   COLUMN 7
    COLUMN 2   COLUMN 4   COLUMN 6

LINE 6.
AUDIO OUTPUT VOLTAGE
WHICH APPEARS ON C4.

LINE 5.
INDIVIDUAL PULSATIONS
OF ELECTRON CURRENT
THROUGH DIODE V2B.

LINE 4.
VOLTAGE WAVEFORM
APPLIED TO PLATE OF
DIODE V2B.

LINE 3.
INDIVIDUAL PULSATIONS
OF ELECTRON CURRENT
THROUGH DIODE V2A.

LINE 2.
VOLTAGE WAVEFORM APPLIED
TO PLATE OF DIODE V2A.

LINE 1.
FM CARRIER SIGNAL AT CENTER
FREQUENCY OF 4.5 MC

UNDESIRED AMPLITUDE INCREASE IN
CARRIER SIGNAL OCCURS HERE.

Fig. 7-5. Timing and amplitude relationships between the FM signal, the diode voltages and currents, and the audio output voltage.

131

signal. Variations in signal strength can occur due to unusual atmospheric conditions or temporary aberrations in the amplification processes carried out earlier in the receiver, such as in the video amplifier or the sound-IF amplifier. Any such variations in amplitude are spurious and bear no relation whatsoever to the intelligence conveyed by the carrier to the receiver. The most obvious means of eliminating amplitude variations (usually called modulation) is to amplify the incoming signal so that all portions of it will have some predetermined minimum amplitude, and then to cut off, or limit, all attempts of the signal to exceed that predetermined value.

The ratio detector of Fig. 7-1 is not preceded by a conventional limiting stage; it employs a novel method for accomplishing the same purpose or function. This method is embodied in the RC filter network connected to the cathode of diode V2A. Capacitor C5 is a large electrolytic capacitor (about 2 microfarads) and R5 is approximately 25,000 ohms. The product of these two components, which determines the time-constant of the combination, is 1/20 of a second. This is a "long" time period when compared to the cycle duration of typical audio frequencies; therefore a positive voltage, which will not vary from audio cycle to audio cycle, will appear on the upper plate of C5. This voltage results from the continual loss of electrons due to the current being drawn into the cathode of V2A. This positive voltage constitutes a fixed biasing voltage for the ratio detector as a whole. For example, if the peak positive value of the red waveform in Line 2 of Fig. 7-5 is 1 volt from the center-line axis (meaning 2 volts peak to peak), then the upper plate of C5 will charge up to a value of $+2$ volts. The reference voltage for the audio output on the upper plate of C4 will become half of this, or $+1$ volt. The red voltage waveforms of Lines 2 and 4 (Fig. 7-5) will vary around this reference value. Diode V2A will then conduct only on the positive peaks, or tips, of the red waveform in Line 2, and diode V2B will conduct only on the negative peaks of the red waveform in Line 4.

During the negative half-cycles represented by Columns 2 and 4, we have seen how the positive voltage on C4 decreases. The amount of this decrease in voltage on C4 is dependent on the differences in amplitude of the red waveforms of Lines 2 and 4 during these time periods. As the amplitudes in Line 2 increase, those in Line 4 decrease, and these amplitude changes are regulated strictly by the amount of frequency deviation of the carrier from the center frequency.

Now let us consider what happens in the ratio detector when some unwanted amplitude modulation occurs. Columns 6 and 7 of Fig. 7-5 have been included to show what happens to the various waveforms. The input signal shown in Line 1 has been increased in strength by about 50%. This means that both of the input waveforms (solid and dotted blue) in Figs. 7-3 and 7-4 are stronger by that amount. Their two resultants (the red waveforms) are proportionately increased in strength. These increased amplitudes are shown in the red waveforms of Lines 2 and 4. Each positive swing of the red waveform in Line 2 causes increased conduction through V2A, *to a greater extent* than occurs in Columns 2 and 4. This would seem to deliver an excess of electrons onto C4, thereby distorting the true magnitude of the negative half-cycles of voltage which should accumulate there. However, the amplitude of the individual cycles of voltage in Line 4 which are applied to the cathode of the lower diode also increase during this time period. V2B also conducts more electrons than were indicated during the negative half-cycle of Columns 2 and 4. Thus a means exists for draining off the excess electrons received from the upper diode before they can accumulate on C4 and increase the negative voltage which should normally be created there during a negative half-cycle.

During the positive half-cycle represented by Column 7, both of the red waveforms in Lines 2 and 4 will also be proportionately increased in amplitude by the unwanted change in amplitude of the incoming signal shown in Line 1. This increase in amplitude causes an increased conduction of electrons through diode V2B over and above that normally expected during a positive half-cycle. The enlarged pulsations of diode current through V2B during this period are the green pulses in Line 5. This would seem to create an excessively large deficiency of electrons, and therefore a positive voltage, on the upper plate of C4. However, this abnormality in output voltage on C4 is counteracted by the increased quantity of electrons coming into C4 through V2A. These enlarged pulsations of current through V2A are indicated in Column 7 of Line 3.

The resultant voltages on C4 during these two half-cycles of audio end up being just about what they would have been if the unwanted amplitude modulation shown in Line 1 had not occurred. The output voltage is shown in green in Line 6. It varies around the reference value of +1 volt, and is unaffected by amplitude modulation of the signal. Thus, the function served by a conventional limiting circuit has been achieved by the RC network connected between the cathode of V2A and ground.

The audio voltage which appears on C4 is frequently called a *differential voltage*, because its magnitude is proportional to the differing amounts of voltage delivered to or withdrawn from C4 by the conducting diodes. Fig. 7-1 is only one of several variations of ratio detectors; it has been presented here because of its relative simplicity compared to earlier versions. The title of ratio detector stems from one of the earlier versions in which the audio-output voltage was claimed to be proportional to two voltages developed across separate resistor-capacitor load combinations.

The increased amplitude shown in Columns 6 and 7 persists for only one cycle, and normal aberrations in amplitude would persist for relatively few audio cycles. Consequently, even though diode V2A passes increased electron current for these few audio cycles, these extra electrons are withdrawn from the upper plate of electrolytic capacitor C5. This is such a large capacitor that it requires many trillions of positive ions to charge it up to its indicated value of +2 volts. It can give up the additional electrons required by a few abnormally large pulsations of diode current without a significant change in voltage. If the increased amplitude in signal strength shown in Columns 6 and 7 persisted for a very long period of time, such as might occur when switching from a faraway station to a close one, then the upper plate of capacitor C5 would permanently charge to some higher value of positive voltage. The reference voltage which appears on the upper plate of C4 would also increase until it equaled half of the value of the voltage on C5. The audio voltage waveform in Line 6 of Fig. 7-5 would then vary around this new reference value.

Because of the fact that the upper plate of C5 assumes a positive voltage which is proportional to the incoming-signal strength, it can be used as a source of automatic gain control (AGC) voltage. However, if it were so used, it would have to be applied to the cathodes of the various amplifiers rather than to the control grids. This is because it increases in the positive direction as the signal strength increases. Positive voltages applied to amplifier cathodes cause decreases in amplifier gain; thus, the desired effect from an AGC circuit when confronted by an increase in signal strength would be obtained using this voltage.

The audio voltage which appears on C4 (Fig. 7-1) drives electron current in and out of coupling capacitor C7, and up and down through volume-control resistor R6 toward ground. Thus, an audio voltage is developed across R6. Any portion of this voltage may be tapped off R6 for subsequent amplification by the two audio amplifier stages (V3 and V4).

When this audio-output current (solid green) is driven upward through R6, it is also driven to the right through C8, and downward through the grid-driving resistor (R7). An alternate picture of the voltage condition one half of an audio cycle later than that shown in the main schematic is given directly below C4 in Fig. 7-1. The main schematic is for a negative half-cycle, and the lower conditions are for a positive half-cycle. During these positive half-cycles the audio current (solid green) will be drawn away from the left plate of C7, downward through R6, and upward through R7 onto the right-hand plate of C8.

Since there are no new and unique principles employed in the audio amplifiers which have not already been described in connection with the sound systems in Chapter 6, the two amplifiers constructed around V3 and V4 will not be discussed here. For a comprehensive discussion on the subject of amplification refer to a companion text in this Electronic Circuit Action Series on *Amplifier Circuit Actions*.

Sound De-emphasis

A similar version of this receiver may employ the audio output capacitor connected from the left-hand terminal of R4 (Fig. 7-1) to ground. R4 and C4 would then provide the function known as *de-emphasis* of high audio frequencies. The reactance of any capacitor decreases as the frequency increases. As the audio-frequency voltage on C4 increases in frequency, the reactance of C4 decreases. Another way of saying this is that C4 will begin to short-circuit the higher audio-frequencies to ground, rather than permitting them to flow only in and out of C7. This technique is used deliberately, because in the original transmission of the sound signals the higher-frequency sounds were pre-emphasized. That is, they were intentionally increased in amplitude in comparison with the lower-frequency sounds. Pre-emphasis is employed because much of the audio-frequency interference generated during the modulation process at the transmitter, and within the receiver, consists of the higher audio frequencies. Pre-emphasis within the transmitter improves the signal-to-noise ratio of the higher audio frequencies, but it obviously requires the de-emphasis process within the receiver to restore both high- and low-frequency audio tones to their correct proportions with respect to each other.

PHASE DISCRIMINATOR OPERATION

Fig. 7-6 shows a typical phase discriminator circuit for the demodulation of the frequency-modulated sound-IF signal. This circuit differs from the ratio detector of Fig. 7-1, primarily in the arrangement of the diodes. The two diodes in Fig. 7-6 are connected in parallel with each other so that separate currents flow through each one. In Fig. 7-1 the two diodes were in series with each other so that whatever electron current flowed through one of them eventually had to flow through the other one also. The

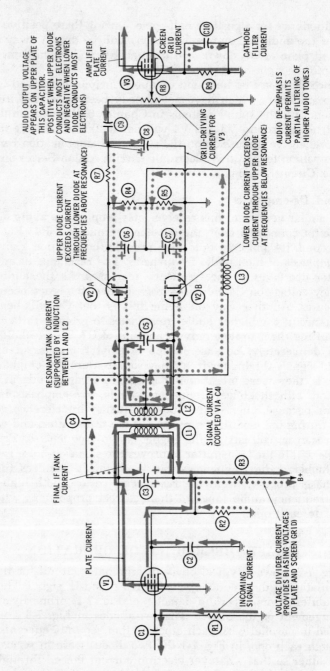

Fig. 7-6. Operation of a sound system employing a phase discriminator.

audio-amplifying portion of the receiver which contains the phase discriminator network is similar in nature to those previously discussed, so they will not be redescribed.

Identification of Components

This circuit includes the following functional components:

L1—Final sound-IF transformer primary winding.
L2—Final sound-IF transformer secondary winding.
L3—Radio-frequency choke between secondary tank and diode load resistors.
R1—Grid-driving resistor for V1.
R2, R3—Voltage-divider network for biasing plate and screen grid of V1.
R4—Load resistor for diode V2A.
R5—Load resistor for diode V2B.
R7—Part of high-frequency de-emphasis network.
R8—Manual volume control and grid-driving resistor for V3.
R9—Cathode-biasing resistor for V3.
C1—Input coupling capacitor from video amplifier.
C2—Screen-grid filtering and decoupling capacitor.
C3—Part of tuned primary tank circuit.
C4—Coupling capacitor between tuned primary and center tap of secondary winding.
C5—Part of tuned secondary tank circuit.
C6—Integrating capacitor across diode-load resistor R4.
C7—Integrating capacitor across diode-load resistor R5.
C8—High-frequency de-emphasis capacitor.
C9—Coupling capacitor to V3.
C10—Cathode-bypass capacitor for V3.
V1—Final sound-IF amplifier tube.
V2A—Upper diode used for demodulation of FM signal.
V2B—Lower diode used for demodulation.
V3—Audio-amplifier tube.

Functions Performed

The major functions performed by this type of circuit are identical to those performed by the ratio detector. These functions are:

1. Amplification of the FM sound-IF signal received from the video amplifier or video-output stage.
2. Coupling of this amplifier signal by two separate and independent means from the primary tank (C3 and L1) to the diode discriminator network.

3. Development of an audio-output voltage at the upper terminal of R4, and coupling of this voltage to the audio amplifiers.
4. De-emphasis of the higher audio frequencies.

Identification of Currents

The electron currents which flow in this circuit during normal operation, and the colors they are shown in, are as follows:

1. Pentode plate currents through V1 and V3 (solid red).
2. Screen-grid currents through these same tubes (also in solid red).
3. Voltage-divider current through R2 and R3 (dotted red).
4. Input signal current from video amplifier (solid blue).
5. Resonant tank currents in primary and secondary tank circuits (also in solid blue).
6. Signal current capacitively coupled from primary tank to center tap of secondary winding (dotted blue).
7. Pulsating direct currents through the two diodes (dotted green).
8. Audio-output current (solid green).

Details of Operation

The operation of the IF amplifier (V1) is straightforward and similar to the one discussed in connection with the ratio detector circuit. The input signal current (solid blue) is driven from the video amplifier and moves in and out of C1 and up and down through R1 at the instantaneous frequency of the FM sound signal. The center frequency for this signal is 4.5 mc; however, the modulation may cause it to vary between the limits of 4.475 to 4.525 mc. The plate current through this tube (solid red) is caused to pulsate at the instantaneous input frequency; these pulsations set up an oscillation of electrons between L1 and C3, which are resonant at the center frequency of 4.5 mc.

The secondary tank circuit (L2 and C5) is also resonant at this same frequency. Since L1 and L2 are two windings of a transformer, the inductive coupling process which goes on between them sets up and sustains another oscillation (solid blue) of electrons in the secondary tank circuit. This is the last spot at which the FM sound signal appears in the receiver. In Fig. 7-6 this secondary current is moving downward through L2 so as to deliver electrons to the lower plate of C5 and to withdraw electrons from the upper plate. If this were the only signal current flowing in these secondary tank components, the positive voltage indicated by plus signs on the upper plate of C5 would cause electrons to flow through V2A from cathode to plate. Half a cycle later this same amount of positive voltage would have been built up on the lower plate of C5, causing V2B to conduct an equal quantity of electrons. The net amount of electron current available to flow away from the area of each diode plate toward the junction of load resistors R4 and R5 (through L3) would be equal, so that equal and opposite voltages would be developed across the two resistors. These two equal and opposite voltages add up to zero.

Even when the FM signal varies above and below its center frequency, the condition of equal conduction of the two diodes during alternate half-cycles would not be disturbed, since the two diode plates would be driven to equal values of positive voltage by the tank voltage. Consequently, without the additional means of coupling provided by C4, the rest of the circuit cannot function as a demodulator. Capacitor C4 connects the top of the primary tank circuit with the center tap of secondary winding L2. This results in applying the primary tank voltage, simultaneously in the same phase, to the plates of the two diodes. This statement may be clarified by explaining that when the voltage at the top of the primary tank is negative, as it is in Fig. 7-6, a negative voltage is simultaneously applied to the plates of V2A and V2B. The physical means by which this is accomplished is a minute flow of electron current (dotted blue) from the top of the primary tank onto the left-hand plate of C4, with an equal quantity being driven away from the right-hand plate through the two halves of center-tapped inductor L2. This flow through the two halves of L2 is, of course, in opposite directions toward the two diode plates. A half-cycle later, when the voltage at the top of the primary tank has become positive, this minute electron current will reverse its direction and be drawn toward L1. This action will simultaneously draw electrons away from both diode plates, making them positive, and causing both diodes to conduct equal amounts of electrons.

If this were the only signal current flowing in the discriminator, it could not function as a demodulator, because with each positive half-cycle of the FM signal, whether it is occurring at the center frequency, or above or below it, both diodes will conduct equal quantities of electrons, so that equal and opposite voltages will be developed across load resistors R4 and R5. They would again add up to zero so that the output voltage measured across *both* resistors (from ground to the top of resistor R4) would be zero.

The dual-diode circuit of Fig. 7-6 will function as a detector only when the FM signal is coupled to the diode circuit by both of the methods just discussed—transformer coupling between L1 and L2, and capacitive coupling via C4. The waveform diagrams of Figs. 7-2, 7-3, and 7-4 apply with equal validity to this phase-discriminator circuit. When the FM signal is exactly on its center frequency, the oscillation in the secondary tank circuit will be exactly 90° out of phase with the oscillation in the primary. This is indicated in Fig. 7-2. The solid blue waveform achieves its maximum positive value exactly a quarter of a cycle *after* the dotted blue waveform reaches its peak in Line 1, and in Line 2 it reaches its peak a quarter of a cycle *before* the dotted blue waveform reaches its peak. The resultant waveform (red) in Line 1 is the voltage applied to the plate of upper diode V2A, and the red waveform of Line 2 is the voltage applied to the plate of lower diode V2B. The positive portions of each of these waveforms cause the respective diodes to conduct.

When V2A conducts, its plate-current path takes it from the cathode to the plate within the diode, downward through the upper half of L2 to the center tap, through L3, and upward through R4 to the cathode. These electrons, in flowing upward through R4, develop a positive voltage at the top of this resistor. This positive voltage is indicated by plus signs on the upper plate of C6.

When V2B conducts, its current flows from cathode to plate within the diode, upward through the lower half of L2 to the center tap, through L3, and downward through load resistor R5 to the cathode again. In flowing downward through R5 a voltage is developed across this resistor which is negative at the top and positive at the bottom. These voltages are indicated by appropriate plus and minus signs on C7.

When these two diode currents flow through their respective load resistors (R4 and R5) in exactly equal amounts, then equal voltages must be developed across the two resistors. Since the currents flow in *opposite* directions through these resistors (upward through R4 and downward through R5), the sum of these voltages, which is measured from the top of R4 to ground, must be zero. This condition will be satisfied only when the two input signals are in exact phase quadrature, as shown in Fig. 7-2. This happens only when the tuned tanks are operated at their natural resonant frequency of 4.5 mc.

When the signal deviates above the center frequency, the condition shown in Fig. 7-3 exists. The two input waveforms *as measured at the top of the tank* move closer in phase, whereas the two input waveforms which exist at the bottom of the tank move farther apart in phase. The most extreme cases which could occur would be for the two voltage waveforms at the top of the tank (shown in Line 1) to be exactly in phase with each other, while the two voltage waveforms at the bottom of the tank would be exactly a half-cycle out of phase. The resultant (red) waveform in the first case would then be twice the amplitude of the input waveforms, and the resultant in the second case would be zero— in other words, a straight line. The lower diode would not conduct at all under these conditions. These extremes are not even approached in normal discriminator operation.

During operation above resonance, the plate of V2A will be driven to more positive values than the lower diode plate, because of the differing sizes of the applied waveforms (red in Fig. 7-3). V2A will conduct more electrons than V2B. Thus, the amount of current flowing upward through R4 will exceed that which flows downward through R5 and a net positive voltage will be developed at the upper terminal of R4. This can be described as a positive half-cycle of audio voltage. In order to meet this temporary demand for electrons to flow into the upper diode, electrons will be drawn away from the left plate of C9 and upward through grid-driving resistor R8. This creates a positive voltage at the grid of V3.

Fig. 7-4 shows what happens to the two signal voltages when the signal deviates below the center frequency. The two input waveforms at the top of the tank move farther apart in phase so that their resultant waveform (red) decreases in amplitude. At the same time the voltages being applied to the bottom of the tank have moved closer together in phase, and their resultant waveform (red) is greater. This applies a higher positive voltage to the plate of V2B, so it conducts more electrons than V2A. This develops a negative voltage at the top of R5 which is greater in magnitude than the positive voltage being developed across R4, so that a net negative voltage exists at the top of R4. This is a negative half-cycle of audio voltage, and it is characterized by a downward movement of electron current through R8.

R7 and C8 constitute a de-emphasis circuit for partially attenuating the higher audio frequencies in the sound signal. Because the impedance of this capacitor, like any capacitor, decreases as the frequency increases, the higher audio frequencies will be partially bypassed or filtered to ground through C8, and smaller amounts of current will be driven up and down through R8 at these frequencies.

In addition to accumulating an audio voltage on the upper plate of C6, this capacitor along with C7 serves to filter out the IF pulsations which characterize the current through the upper detector. While one audio cycle may last for a thousandth of a second, there will be four thousand or more pulsations of diode current during this period. Each time one of these pulsations goes through the diode, there will be an upward movement of electrons from ground through C7 and C6. When each pulsation stops, the electron movement through these capacitors reverses. No comparable requirement exists to provide a filter function for the cathode of lower diode V2B, since this electrode is connected to ground.

C8 also functions as an IF filter capacitor, but to a lesser extent. As each pulsation of electron current is drawn into the upper diode, some electrons will be drawn through R7. These electrons must be drawn from someplace, and the only two available paths are from the upper plate of C8 and the left-hand plate of C9. If the electrons are drawn from C9, however, an equal number must be drawn upward through R8 in the process. Because the reactance of C8 is much lower at the sound carrier frequency of 4.5 mc than the impedance of C9 in series with R8, the great bulk of this filtering action will occur through C8 to ground.

The amount by which the carrier signal deviates above and below the center frequency is what determines the loudness of the final audio signal.

REVIEW QUESTIONS

1. In the ratio detector circuit shown in Fig. 7-1, name the two alternating voltages which are applied to the diodes and state where they come from?

2. When the signal is exactly at the center frequency, what is the phase relationship between these two voltages?

3. If these two applied voltages have exactly equal amplitudes, what is the phase relationship and the resulting voltage (shown in the red waveform in Fig. 7-2) between each one when at the center frequency?

4. If the basic frequency moves *above* the center frequency, do the two driving voltages which are applied to the *upper diode* move closer together or farther apart in their phase? Does this increase or decrease the total amount of conduction from the upper diode?

5. If the upper diode conducts fewer electrons than the lower diode, what happens to the voltage on the upper plate of capacitor C4—does it become more positive or less positive?

6. What feature of circuit construction determines that the voltage on the upper plate will be a positive voltage at all times?

7. In the phase discriminator circuit of Fig. 7-6, which of the two diodes conducts the greater quantity of electron current when the frequency deviates below the center frequency? What is the fundamental difference in the "conduction patterns" of the two diodes in this phase discriminator and the two diodes in the ratio detector of Fig. 7-1?

8. Where does the audio voltage make its first identifiable appearance in the phase discriminator circuit? How about in the ratio detector circuit?

Chapter 8

POWER SUPPLIES

Before any circuit in a TV receiver (or any type of electronic equipment for that matter) can function, the proper DC voltages must be applied to the plate and screen-grid elements of the various tubes. The normal power supplied to homes in the United States is 117-volts AC. It is the function of the power supply to step this 117-volts AC up to the value necessary to operate the tubes, and to convert the AC to DC. Many circuits can be used to accomplish this purpose. The ones given in this chapter are typical of those encountered in modern TV receivers. A more comprehensive description of power supply circuits is given in a companion volume of this Basic Electronics Series, *Detector and Rectifier Circuits*.

FULL-WAVE RECTIFIER WITH TRANSFORMER

Figs. 8-1 and 8-2 show two identical diagrams of a typical transformer-type power supply which employs a voltage-doubler circuit. In addition, the audio-output amplifier is used as a voltage divider to obtain a lower voltage. The techniques found in this circuit enjoy wide usage in modern receivers.

Identification of Components

These two circuits (amplifier and rectifier) are made up of the following components:

Rectifier Portion

    L1, L2—Primary and secondary windings, respectively, of power transformer.

L5—Output filter choke.

C1—Filter capacitor across transformer primary.

C2, C3—Series capacitors used for voltage doubling.

C4, C5—Output filter capacitors.

C6—Output filter capacitor for reduced voltage output.

R1—High resistance to ground on primary side of power transformer.

R2—Low-value fusing resistor.

R3—Filtering and voltage-dropping resistor.

M1, M2—Rectifying diodes.

Amplifier Portion

L3, L4—Primary and secondary windings of audio-output transformer.

C7—Grid input capacitor.

C8—Cathode filter capacitor, also serves as output capacitor for 135-volt source.

C9—Plate to cathode filter capacitor for stray RF and IF currents.

C10—Serves, along with C8, as a decoupling capacitor between amplifier and 270-volt source.

R4—Part of voltage-divider network for biasing amplifier grid.

R5—Grid-driving resistor, also part of voltage-divider network.

R6—Grid-isolating resistor.

R7—Cathode-biasing resistor.

V1—Audio-output tube.

Identification of Currents

The various electron currents at work in this combination of circuits may be identified as follows:

1. Input current from household supply (dotted blue).
2. Power-transformer secondary current (also in dotted blue).
3. Rectified current through M1 (dotted red).
4. Rectified current through M2 (solid red).
5. Filter currents between ground and C2, C3, C4, C5, C6, and C8 (also in solid red).
6. Load currents flowing into each of the three output voltage points (also in dotted red).
7. Grid-driving current for audio amplifier (solid green).
8. Audio-output current through winding L4 (also in solid green).
9. Amplifier plate current (also in solid red).

Details of Operation

A typical television receiver requires at least three values of high positive voltages. In the circuit shown in Figs. 8-1 and 8-2, these three values are 270, 250, and 135 volts. The first two of these values are close together and are usually achieved by a conventional voltage-divider device represented here by R3. The third voltage, which is considerably lower than the first two, can also be achieved by this means. However, this method is somewhat wasteful of power and it also produces excessive heat within the receiver. An alternative means is depicted in Figs. 8-1 and 8-2. The final audio-amplifier tube is used as a voltage-divider device across the high positive output voltage. The audio-output tube is a heavy-current tube, meaning that it has a large amount of plate current flowing through it. The tubes served by the 135-volt output developed at the cathode of V1 are all low-current tubes; all of their plate currents must eventually flow as plate current through V1. The plate currents of these other tubes are shown as the load current entering the 135-volt source from the right.

The house supply current (input) flows up and down through L1 at the basic power frequency of 60 cps. Its movements cause a companion current to flow down and up through secondary winding L2. An induced voltage will be associated with this secondary current; the polarity of this induced voltage is indicated as positive, or plus, in Fig. 8-2 and as negative, or minus, in Fig. 8-1. Both of the primary and secondary currents are shown in dotted blue.

When the upper end of L2 is made negative by this induced voltage (Fig. 8-1), electron current (dotted red) will flow through M1 in a downward direction from cathode to anode. These electrons must be drawn from the upper plate of C3, resulting in a deficiency of electrons (positive voltage) on the upper plate of this capacitor. This positive voltage is approximately equal to the peak value of the negative voltage at the upper end of L2.

During the next succeeding half-cycle, when the upper end of L2 is made positive by the induced voltage (Fig. 8-2), electrons cannot flow downward through M1. However, they will be drawn from right to left through M2, since the anode of this diode will now be more positive than its cathode. These electrons are drawn simultaneously from the two output points (270 and 250 volts) and through the voltage-divider (R5 and R4). As electrons are drawn through M2, an additional electron deficiency, or positive voltage, will be created on the upper plates of C2, C4, and C5. This positive voltage will be almost equal to twice the peak value of the induced voltage appearing across L2. If this induced voltage is varying 135 volts on either side of its center value, then the voltage at the top of C2 actually varies between values of 270 volts and zero volts. The reason for this is that the entire area between C3 and the junction of the two diodes becomes flooded with the voltage value of 135 volts, so the alternating secondary voltage varies around this value rather than around zero. Thus, the peak input voltage is "doubled" by the series capacitor arrangement of C2 and C3. M2 will not conduct for an entire half-cycle; it conducts only at those moments when the induced voltage makes the anode of M2 *more positive* than the voltage on the

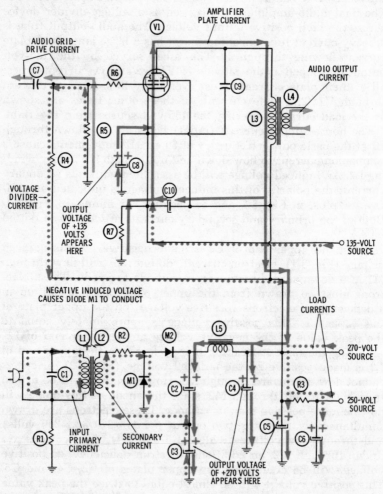

Fig. 8-1. Operation of transformer power supply—first half-cycle.

upper plate of C2. All five of the electrolytic capacitors in this circuit (C2 through C6) are serving a filter function. In Fig. 8-1, when M2 does not conduct, the positive voltages built up on the upper plates of these capacitors continue to draw electron current from the various loads, with the result that electrons flow onto the upper plates of these capacitors and drive additional electrons downward through ground from the lower plates. In Fig. 8-2, when there is a sudden demand for an excessive quantity of electrons, they are drawn from the upper plates of the capacitors so that other electrons are drawn upward from ground

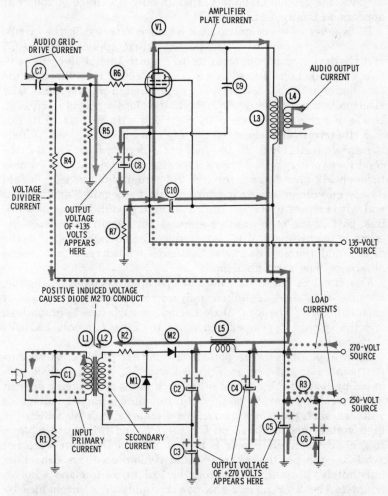

Fig. 8-2. Operation of transformer power supply—alternate half-cycle.

toward the lower plates. These actions constitute two successive half-cycles of filter action, the purpose of which is to draw current smoothly from the loads, rather than in pulsations. Of course, in any power supply such as the one in Figs. 8-1 and 8-2 there will always be a certain amount of pulsation in the output. The amount, or degree, to which pulsations occur in the currents drawn from the various loads in any equipment, such as a receiver, is usually referred to as the *ripple factor*.

In order to slightly reduce the 270-volt output, resistor R3 is provided. The load current drawn through R3 causes the necessary voltage drop of 20 volts so that an output voltage of 250 volts appears on the upper plate of C6.

R2 is a very low-value resistor which is inserted in the circuit as a protective device. When power is first applied (before C3 and C2 have had an opportunity to acquire their values of positive voltage) excessive electron current could flow through the two diodes in the same direction as indicated in the diagrams. The electron current flowing through R2 develops a voltage across it. In Fig. 8-1 this is positive at its right end with respect to its left end; therefore, the effect of the high negative induced voltage is somewhat nullified. In the half-cycle depicted by Fig. 8-2 the conditions are reversed. Here a heavy electron current coming through M2 and flowing through R2 (from right to left) would develop a voltage across it which would be negative at the right end with respect to the left end. This voltage nullifies, or neutralizes, part of the high positive induced voltage. In both cases the effect of the presence of R2 is to reduce the voltage applied to the diodes and thereby decrease the excessive current that would otherwise flow through them.

The effect of R2 during normal operation becomes negligible, because each diode conducts only momentarily at the peak of each half-cycle. The total diode current in each case is much less, and the voltage developed across R2 by these currents becomes very small.

Some type of resistive path to ground from the positive output points is necessary. In Figs. 8-1 and 8-2, such a path is provided by R4 and R5. Several other such paths are usually present in a typical receiver. In addition to providing a partial voltage or voltages, such paths also provide a discharge path by which the high voltage accumulated on C2, C4, C5, and C6 may discharge to ground when the power is turned off. If a DC path were not available, the positive charge would remain on these capacitors indefinitely, presenting a serious hazard to technicians who attempt to check or service the power supply. The mechanics by which this discharge action occurs is an upward flow of electrons from ground, such as is shown in the diagrams, flowing through R5 and R6 to the upper plates of these capacitors until they have completely neutralized the positive output voltage.

VOLTAGE-DIVIDER ACTION

The plate of audio amplifier V1 is connected to the 270-volt output point. This tube plate current originates at ground below resistor R7, and in flowing upward through R7 a voltage of about 135 volts is developed. This becomes the cathode voltage, and it is also the output point for the power-supply source of 135 volts. The grid of V1 is placed at about the same value of positive voltage by virtue of the voltage-divider current (dotted red) which flows upward through R5 and downward through R4 toward the 270-volt source. All of this voltage-divider current eventually flows through M2 and M1 to return to ground.

The grid-driving current (solid green) flows up and down through R5 at the audio frequency being received and amplified. In Fig. 8-1 it is being drawn upward through R5, thus making the top of this resistor positive with respect to the bottom. (This voltage is *in addition* to the permanent positive voltage created at the top of R5 by the voltage-divider current.) Fig. 8-1 depicts a positive half of an audio cycle; therefore, the plate current through V1 will be increased substantially. In Fig. 8-2 this driving current is being pushed downward through R5 toward ground so that a negative component of voltage will be developed at the top of this resistor. This negative voltage causes a significant reduction in the quantity of plate current flowing through the tube. These fluctuations in plate current flowing downward through primary winding L3 in the output transformer cause a true alternating current (solid green) to be induced in secondary winding L4. This current is the audio-output current that drives the speaker. In Fig. 8-1 it is shown increasing in the upward direction through L4, because the plate current is increasing in the downward direction through L3 in response to the positive driving voltage at the grid. In Fig. 8-2, when the negative driving voltage at the grid causes the plate current to decrease, the output current increases *in the downward direction* through L4. In this manner, a pulsating direct current (the plate current) causes an alternating secondary current to flow. This output current moves the speaker diaphragm back and forth at the desired audio frequencies.

The cathode of V1 becomes the point to which certain other tube plates are connected—notably tubes within the tuner and other voltage amplifiers within the video IF strip. The audio-detector tube may also be connected to this point if it requires a B+ voltage. For example, the detectors discussed in Chapter 6 require B+. These tubes are essentially low-current consumers so that the total plate currents of all the tubes connected to this point are only a fraction of the total plate current required by V1. V1 is a power amplifier which draws heavy current; any variations in its plate current, which might be caused by variations in current flow through these various voltage amplifiers, will not appreciably alter the 135-volt cathode voltage appearing on the upper plate of C8. The plate currents (dotted red) from these various other tubes are shown entering the amplifier cathode from the right at the point marked 135-volt source.

A decoupling current will flow back and forth through C10 and C8 at the basic audio frequency. This current flows to the left through C10 when the amplifier plate current increases (Fig. 8-1), and to the right when the plate current decreases (Fig. 8-2). This action prevents these current fluctuations from entering the 270-volt source and thereby affecting all other tubes served by this voltage.

TRANSFORMERLESS POWER SUPPLY

Figs. 8-3 and 8-4 show two alternate half-cycles in the operation of a transformerless power supply which is used in a small portable receiver. This circuit utilizes the voltage-doubling principle in a slightly different manner from that discussed previously.

Identification of Components

The functional components of this circuit are as follows:

L1—Filter choke.
C1, C2—Voltage-doubling capacitors. C2 also serves as a filter capacitor.
C3—Output filter capacitor for 135-volt source.
R1—Small value fusing or protective resistor.
R2—Voltage-divider resistor for reducing output voltage at 135-volt source.
M1, M2—Rectifying diodes.

Identification of Currents

The following currents will flow in this circuit during normal operation.

1. Line current (solid blue).
2. Upper and lower diode currents (solid red).
3. Load current entering 270-volt source (also solid red).

4. Load current entering 135-volt source (dotted red).

5. Inductor and capacitor filter currents (dotted blue).

Details of Operation

Fig. 8-3 depicts what might be called a negative half-cycle of operation, because the input line current (solid blue) is flowing *toward* the rectifier circuit from the power source. It flows up to the left-hand plate of electrolytic capacitor C1, driving an equal number of electrons away from its right-hand plate and downward through lower diode M1 to ground. The downward direction is the low-resistance direction for this diode. None of this current can flow to the right through M2 because this would require it to flow from anode to cathode—the high resistance direction.

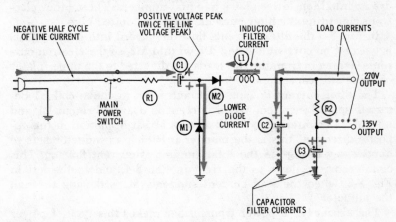

Fig. 8-3. Operation of transformerless power supply—negative half-cycle.

The current that is driven downward through M1 is shown in solid red. The departure of electrons from the right-hand plate of C1 leaves an electron deficiency (a net positive charge) at this point. This positive charge, or voltage, is indicated with red plus signs; the amount of this voltage is approximately equal to the peak negative voltage of the line current. Assume that this is slightly in excess of 135 volts.

Before finishing the discussion of Fig. 8-3, look at Fig. 8-4. Here a positive half-cycle is shown. The line current (solid blue) is being drawn *away* from the left-hand plate of C1 and an equal number of electrons are drawn onto the right-hand plate. These electrons (solid red) can only come from the other side of diode M2. The diode current is drawn simultaneously from several places: from the upper plate of C2, the upper plate of C3 by flowing through R2, and the 270-volt output source. The anode of

M2 is raised to a positive voltage approximately twice the value of the peak line current, because the positive line voltage of 135 volts becomes added to the 135 volts which was created at that point during the preceding negative half-cycle. Since the diode is essentially a short circuit to current flowing from cathode to anode, enough electrons will be drawn through it during this half-cycle to charge the upper plate of C2 to almost 270 volts. The output voltage appears on this capacitor plate in the form of a positive charge (red plus signs). A lesser voltage of about 135 volts appears on the upper plate of C3, and the difference between these two voltage values is "dropped" across R2 by the upward flow of the load current (dotted red). When electrons are drawn away from the upper plates of C2 and C3, other electrons are drawn into their lower plates in equal numbers. These other electrons constitute the filter currents shown in dotted blue.

In Fig. 8-3 the filter currents flow downward into ground. This is because no current is being drawn into M2, so the electron currents coming in from the two loads are diverted to the upper plates of these two capacitors.

The filter current flowing back and forth in choke coil L1 deserves special mention. When current is drawn through L1 and into M2, a countercurrent will always be set in motion in the opposite direction; this is the manner in which an inductor acts to oppose any change in the total amount of current flowing. This countercurrent flows to the right in Fig. 8-4, and to the left in Fig. 8-3, when the load current suddenly stops flowing through the inductor.

The absence of a power transformer makes this type of power supply very attractive from the standpoint of light weight. The

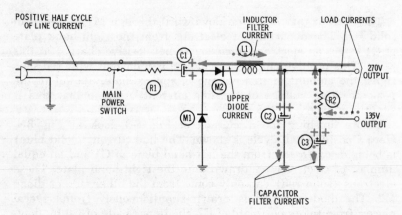

Fig. 8-4. Operation of transformerless power supply—positive half-cycle.

attendant disadvantage is that line current is brought directly up to C1, and the possibility of electric shock is much greater. The presence of the 135-volt output point indicates that this system does not utilize the technique mentioned previously, where the audio-output tube serves as a voltage divider to provide a source of 135 volts to the plates of other tubes. Therefore, all of the plate currents from these tubes must eventually flow upward through R2 to create the 135-volt drop which exists between the two ends of this resistor. This is wasteful of power, and it generates excessive heat within the receiver.

R1 serves the protective function of limiting the initial flow of current toward C1 and M1. At the first instant line power is applied, C1 is a virtual short circuit, and the downward direction through M1 is equivalent to a short circuit at all times. Excessive current would flow through both components during these first moments and M1 would be damaged. R1 is only a few ohms in value; however, this amount of resistance is sufficient to limit the initial flow of line current to a safe value.

REVIEW QUESTIONS

1. Trace the path of the plate current of the audio power amplifier tube (V1) in Figs. 8-1 and 8-2. What useful purpose is served by using this current to develop the positive 135-volt source for the rest of the receiver?

2. Do diodes M1 and M2 conduct simultaneously or alternately? Describe the circuit conditions which must exist in order for each of these diodes to conduct.

3. Give a definition of ripple factor. What is its significance in the transformer power supply of this chapter?

4. Describe how R2 (Figs. 8-1 and 8-2) acts as a protective device. What does it protect against?

5. In the transformerless power supply of Fig. 8-4, how does R1 serve as a protective resistor?

6. What are the advantages and disadvantages of the transformerless power supply over the transformer variety described in this chapter?

INDEX